PRACTICAL UNCERTAINTY

Useful Ideas in Decision-Making, Risk, Randomness & AI

HOSSEIN PISHRO-NIK

Practical Uncertainty
Hossein Pishro-Nik

Produced by Spoonbridge Press
Cover design by Ali Khayati
Illustrations by Sepideh Sakhaeifar
Barbapapa illustration based on copyrighted material and used with permission

First U.S. Edition, 2023
Print ISBN: 978-0-9906372-2-6
Ebook ISBN: 978-0-9906372-3-3

Printed in the U.S.A.

CONTENTS

Chapter 7:
AI and Decision-Making 137

INTRODUCTION

There we were, my wife and I, standing in front of a gorgeous house we were about to call our own. We'd been house-hunting for a while, and on the face of it, this one seemed to satisfy almost all of our criteria. It was perfect. But somehow, we were not happy. For some mysterious reason, we got a bad feeling when we visited the house. Something was wrong, but we could not figure out what it was.

We soon discovered that the reason behind our negative feelings was more unexpected and deeper-seated than I could have anticipated.

I was only two years old when the war started—an eight-year-long war that eventually claimed the lives of more than half a million people. Air raids and missile attacks on my hometown were common. I remember the terrifying sounds of bombs and missiles striking seemingly random areas of the city, sometimes close enough to my neighborhood to shake buildings and shatter windows. I grew up holding my breath and waiting for the next blast.

Many of us who grew up with memories of war have an understandably unfavorable feeling about any sound that reminds us of rockets, bombs, or bullets. As it turned out, there was a shooting range near that perfect house we intended to purchase. Standing in front of the house, we could barely hear the gunshots. The low level of noise was almost nonexistent for the residents of the neighborhood. But apparently not to us. I theorized that our dislike for the house stemmed from the noise from the shooting range subconsciously putting us in a bad mood whenever we visited. We did not even realize the cause until someone casually mentioned the shooting range, and we finally understood where those bad feelings were coming from.

We ended up not buying the house. Was this a good decision? Well, there are several aspects of uncertainty, randomness, and decision-making we can consider in this story.

Let's start with my initial bombing experience. Is it rational to be so worried when living in a city under siege? On the surface, if you were in this situation, it is quite unlikely that you would be directly impacted by an incoming bomb. Say your city has several million residents, and each attack directly impacts a few hundred people or so. The probability of a direct impact right where you're standing at any given moment is less than 1 in 1,000. However, you probably agree that this situation—where lives could be lost in the blink of an eye—is more complicated than a simple probability calculation.

The story of my wife and I deciding not to buy the house exemplifies the idea that our decisions are impacted by a variety of factors, many of which we might not even be aware of. Often we cannot accurately assess the quality of our decisions, even after we make them. Was the nearby shooting range the true reason for our bad feelings about the house? Could other factors have played a role without our knowledge?

Interestingly, even if I had a crystal ball that could have shown me what would have happened had we purchased the house, I still would have had difficulty accurately assessing the quality of our decision not to buy the house due to factors such as hindsight and outcome biases.

Life is messy and full of uncertainty, risk, opportunities, and randomness. Human decision-making is too complex to be addressed with a few general rules. So how do we make sure we are making good decisions under uncertainty? In other words, what can we do to gain an edge in our decision-making processes? This was the question I set out to explore more than a decade ago, and it is the question at the center of this book.

WHAT THIS BOOK IS ABOUT

Practical Uncertainty combines what I found to be the most useful concepts and ideas in uncertainty, risk, randomness, and decision-making; presents them in a coherent, practical, and usable way; and offers intuitive insights to better help you internalize these concepts. It also aims to provide you with an understanding of machine learning (ML) and artificial intelligence (AI) decision-making through the lens of uncertainty.

Randomness and uncertainty are all around us, and they impact us in surprising ways. This book is intended as a practical and educational manual that will help you understand and internalize useful tools for risk-taking and decision-making under uncertainty, both by humans and AI.

WHY I WROTE THIS BOOK

Over the course of two decades in my career as a researcher, in my research, I have heavily used tools from probability, statistics, information theory, and related fields. I even published a textbook on probability. However, over a decade ago, I became seriously interested in how these often-abstract tools can be used in personal and social life. I realized that risk, uncertainty, and randomness are vital parts of business, sports, politics, and almost every personal or societal decision we encounter.

I began researching and attending seminars and workshops on uncertainty and randomness in real life. After a while, I started teaching various university courses on uncertainty, risk, and decision-making that were mostly based on the vast available literature on the subject. I also became interested in using AI decision-making in engineered systems as a part of my research agenda.

Then, to validate my teaching methods, I started to keep track of how I was using the tools I was teaching in my own personal decision-making. The result surprised me: after two years of teaching the course, I could attribute very few of my decisions to my new "expertise" in decision-making, and I realized that very little of what I was teaching now would have helped me make better decisions in the past. What was going on? Did I have it all wrong?

The realization that few of the tools I was teaching my students had proved useful in my own life was a wake-up call for me. If I was not able to use most of these concepts, how useful could they really be to my students? How could I remove the less consequential stuff and focus on the most fundamental and useful concepts for real-life decision-making? That became my primary objective.

I began to notice that a large part of the content I was using in my courses and seminars, although academically interesting, was not usually applicable in practice (at least to my personal decision-making experience). In the end, I stripped away anything that wasn't directly relevant to our daily lives, leaving only those lessons that I or the students in my classes had found helpful.

Slowly, interesting patterns emerged. Finally, I was able to combine these useful but somewhat disparate ideas into a coherent whole and present them in a practical and actionable way. It turned out that it was the *intuitive understanding* of uncertainty and how it impacts our lives that was particularly useful.

I also noted that this foundational look at uncertainty is at the core of machine learning (ML) and AI decision-making. This topic fit very well with the other remaining core content and thus was added to the course (and now to this book). For those unfamiliar with ML, the presentation in this book should be self-contained; for those already familiar, I hope my approach can provide new insights and better understanding.

During this period, on several occasions, I had to make tough life-and-death decisions, which helped a lot in practically evaluating the decision-making strategies described in this book. At the same time, my research group and I were building autonomous systems whose purposes were to make high-impact decisions. For example, we designed a group of autonomous drones that could help in search and rescue operations. A good decision by such autonomous agents could save lives, while a bad decision could have catastrophic consequences.

To develop my research further, I also tried to take all opportunities to gain practical experience with randomness and uncertainty such as engaging in finance and entrepreneurial activities. For example, financial markets are a good place to experience randomness and uncertainty, so I opened an investment account and started to manage my own small portfolio. This was shortly after the 2008 financial crisis, so there was a lot to learn. While I had been familiar with theories of finance for years, taking risks with a sizable portion of my own money was certainly a fruitful experience.

This book is thus the result of my exploration, teaching, and research on decision-making under uncertainty. Everything discussed within it is some concept or trick that my students or I found personally useful in some respect, either directly or by helping to better understand and internalize other useful concepts.

HOW THIS BOOK CAN HELP

There are many admirable books and articles relating to the fields touched upon in this book: chance, uncertainty, risk, decision-making, psychology, and machine learning.

I have greatly benefited from and been influenced by many of these resources. Many of them, combined with my own research, experiences, and research, have shaped the content of this book. However, my hope is that this book can benefit even the readers familiar with the existing excellent body of work for the following reasons.

First, the focus here is mostly on the question "How can I use this in my own personal and work life?" One reason the courses I taught were less effective in the beginning years was that I tried to cover too much. With this in mind, my goal for this book was to identify the most useful concepts and ideas surrounding decision-making under uncertainty, then present them in a concise and usable way.

Second, some insights and techniques in this book might be novel or barely covered elsewhere. For example, I will discuss some practical applications of information theory in decision-making, privacy, and finance that I do not believe have been adequately covered before for the general audience. The combined presentation of human decision-making and machine learning under the umbrella of uncertainty and randomness is similarly uncommon and, I hope, insightful.

One surprising finding from my teachings is that it is easy to misinterpret or misunderstand the implications of some influential works on the topic of uncertainty. For example, I often saw my students drawing gloomy messages from certain readings: that our intuition is hopeless when it comes to randomness and we cannot do much to improve it, or that success is largely determined by luck and we have little influence on our trajectory. I found this extremely frustrating. This kind of thinking was the exact opposite of what I had in mind when sharing this knowledge.

I strongly believe that we *can* work to improve our decision-making. We can better understand uncertainty, and we can use this understanding to increase our chances of achieving our goals. That's why another focus of this book is to reinforce this important conclusion by providing applicable ideas and strategies. Thus, you will find out that this book is written with a somewhat positive outlook in mind. It is not all doom and gloom!

As I mentioned above, a large number of resources that I used over the years, combined with my own research, experiences, and observations, have shaped the content of this book. You'll find a list of relevant resources in the Recommended Reading section at the end. Anything useful in this book should be mostly attributed to the people I learned from, and any shortcomings should be assumed mine.

HOW TO APPROACH THIS BOOK

Practical Uncertainty begins with simple, well-known concepts and gradually moves toward those that are less covered in the existing literature. This structure is intended to make the book easy to read for all audiences. What does that mean for you? If the beginning of the book seems somewhat elementary or even a bit boring, please read on! More exciting topics are soon to come. Even if you are an informed reader on the subject, I recommend reading the entire book, as some treatments of the material might be insightful.

On a related note, a brief word of warning (or perhaps assurance): this is not a rigorous academic science or math book. If you are expecting frequent references to academic journals, discussions on historical data, and so on, this is not the book for you. Instead, I have focused on providing applicable insights and takeaways for life and work.

The book is intended to stimulate pondering as you read. I do not try to sugarcoat or oversimplify anything. Some of the ideas can only be internalized after thinking deeply about them and putting them into practice. That is why I hope you read this book more than once.

Some ideas in the book are based on mathematical arguments. In the interest of making the book accessible, practical, and to the point, I have focused on building intuition and insight rather than providing mathematical or scientific proofs. That said, I have tried hard not to sacrifice useful concepts or mislead readers by oversimplifying things. This means there is, indeed, some minimal but inevitable math in the book. I do briefly explain mathematical concepts as they relate to the topics at hand, but for those readers who dislike math, my hope is that you still find the material useful.

Throughout *Practical Uncertainty*, I have utilized my personal experience, feedback from my students, and my research and observations over the years to continuously improve the presentation of this material. I hope the resulting book is effective and helpful to readers and, hopefully, enjoyable to read.

Now let's get started!

CHAPTER 1:

A WARM-UP: UNLUCKY STREAKS AND MARGINS

A few months into the COVID-19 pandemic, some large organizations and companies found themselves in dire situations and began planning for layoffs, while others in the same industries fared relatively well throughout the pandemic. What was the secret of the companies that managed to stay strong? Well, there are many factors at play here, but a certain property of uncertainty can help us partially answer this question. We will return to this concept shortly, but first, let's start with a quick overview of randomness and uncertainty.

THE BASICS: UNCERTAINTY VIEWED AS RANDOMNESS

This book is about understanding randomness and uncertainty. What do I mean by randomness? I simply mean a lack of certainty. For example, when you start a business, you cannot be sure what your first-year sales will be. Thus, this first year of business is an example of a random experiment. With this view, randomness and uncertainty are essentially the same.

A random experiment doesn't have to be a future event; the event in question could have happened in the past. However, as long as we have uncertainty about the event, we can treat it as a random experiment. For example, the jury in a murder trial is interested in the probability of the defendant's guilt during a past event. Even though the event has already happened, jurors cannot be certain either way of the defendant's guilt.

To summarize this point, any time there is uncertainty or a lack of information about an event, we can consider it a random experiment—and we may be able to use the tools discussed in this book to enhance our decision-making in such scenarios.

A SIMPLE YET INSIGHTFUL RANDOM EXPERIMENT

What is the simplest random experiment? Consider a basic coin toss: you flip a coin, and the outcome is either heads or tails. This simple experiment will be our guide to understanding uncertainty.

You might point out that life is not like tossing a coin or rolling a die. It is not even like poker or any other structured game. And you would be absolutely right. That is why the title of this book is not *How to Live* or something like that. That topic would be too general and too complicated.

So why am I starting with a coin toss example if it does not reflect real life? The simplicity of a coin toss and its limited outcomes can help us develop intuition about randomness and uncertainty that *can* be useful in real-life decision-making. We will build on this intuition throughout the book.

Our discussion on randomness and coin tosses provides a natural way to discuss luck. In anything we do, the outcome is due partly to skill and partly to luck. In this view, a chance occurrence could be interpreted as luck, so we may be able to gain insight by tossing some coins. Our first insight relates to random patterns.

PATTERNS AND LUCK

Every morning when I make my latte, I manage to create a new pattern or shape in the foam. One day it might be a flower, the next day a famous person, and so on. I never practiced this art; I have never worked at a coffee shop. So what is my secret? It's easy: I pour the milk foam randomly over the coffee, and after I am done, I try to identify a pattern. Sure enough, I always find one.

Of course, if you ask me beforehand to create a certain shape, you will be disappointed. Randomness tends to create patterns, and we humans are masters of identifying patterns. Let's investigate this issue more carefully and see how we can effectively use it in our decision-making. To do so, we use our coin-tossing experiment to gain intuition.

PATTERNS IN COIN TOSSES: RUNS AND STREAKS

Let's toss a coin 100 times and observe the sequence of heads and tails to look for patterns. The easiest patterns we might perceive are streaks (or runs) of heads or tails. More specifically, a streak is a sequence of consecutive identical outcomes. For example, HHH is a streak length of three,[1] since it represents three heads in a row.

Consider the result of our 100 coin tosses. How likely is it that somewhere in that sequence we observe a streak length of six—that is, six heads in a row or six tails in a row? Many of us might guess this probability to be less than 50%, but it happens more often than you'd think; the correct answer is more than 80%. What does this tell us? It simply says that streaks resulting from randomness are more likely than what we might naturally expect. See figure 1.1.

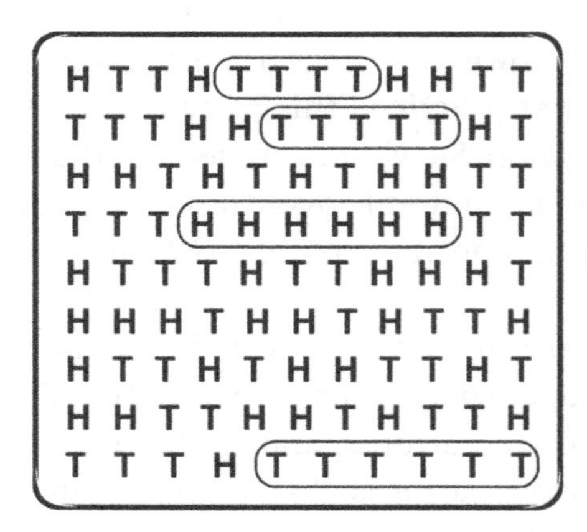

Figure 1.1. The result of 100 coin tosses. A typical random sequence could contain long streaks or runs, i.e., consecutive heads or consecutive tails.

1 Here H represents the coin landing heads up.

According to psychologists, if you were to ask a person to write down a random sequence of heads or tails, they would likely not produce a long streak of consecutive heads or tails. In reality, though, such *clustering*—long random sequences of similar events—does happen. Now, how can we use this observation in real life?

This prevalence of clustering implies that streaks of good and bad luck are inevitable in life and business, but we tend to underestimate their likelihood and length. We need to be prepared to handle this phenomenon and even take advantage of it.

If we can expect certain bad events to sometimes occur consecutively, we should not be surprised or disappointed when they do. We know these clusters of unlucky events simply happen at random. Just by understanding this, we can significantly toughen ourselves against such misfortunes. Rather than becoming depressed after a series of unfortunate events, expecting and planning for these situations can help us cope with them.

One caveat, though: we should make sure we do not mistake bad luck (randomness) with bad planning or bad strategy (unpreparedness). For example, I had a high school friend who never studied for his exams. Instead, he prayed to God to help him *cheat* on the exams! Needless to say, God did not respond to his absurd prayers. My friend's poor results were the consequence not of bad luck but of his lack of preparation.

Although most of us have better judgment than my friend, I share this example as a reminder. We should make sure the misfortune we occasionally experience is not because of our own misguided strategies. Psychologists have observed that we tend to overestimate the role of bad luck in our failures and, at the same time, underestimate the role of good luck in our success. Being aware of these tendencies helps us better manage our situations.

The fact is, bad luck does occasionally cluster, and knowledge of this fact is the first helpful tool we can use to cope with streaks of negative events. In fact, tough times are usually opportunities for improvement. Channeling our frustration into overcoming obstacles and finding new opportunities seems to be a helpful strategy for weathering bad times.

You have probably heard stories of people turning bad luck into great success, so I won't bore you with them here. Instead, let's talk about the next tool for dealing with unlucky streaks. I believe it is one of the most effective tools we can use to deal with bad luck and uncertainty in our lives.

THE VALUE OF MARGINS AND SOME MISCONCEPTIONS

An important strategy in dealing with randomness and uncertainty is including enough margin when planning our days, projects, and business endeavors. Here *margin* refers to any redundancy, extra capacity, buffer, or leeway that helps to soften the blow when unfortunate events occur.

An important point here is that we tend to underestimate the required margin for a situation in the same way we tend to underestimate the length of streaks in the coin toss example. During the COVID-19 pandemic, many large organizations quickly ran into insurmountable problems, in part because they did not implement enough margin in their plans. When running a business, it is a good idea to investigate how the business would survive a few unexpectedly bad months, then take actions to increase buffers and margins to increase your ability to survive.

Here is another important point about uncertainty: we are most vulnerable to events that we do not see coming. These unpredictable outlier events could appear out of nowhere and have big consequences. Nassim Taleb, mathematical statistician and essayist, refers to these events as Black Swans and points out how important they are in our lives. Things that have never happened in the past and of which we are completely oblivious do indeed happen, and they can hurt us.

Sounds horrible, right? Well, implementing margins is one of our best defenses against negative Black Swans. For example, financial advisers always suggest building a sizable emergency fund and limiting debt, both examples of incorporating margins into personal finance. We cannot accurately predict what sort of emergencies we might face in the future, but we can know that significant savings can potentially help us weather such storms.

It is also a good idea to include a decent margin when planning for projects by scheduling more time than we think we'll need. As another everyday example, if you are traveling somewhere or you have an appointment, it's always good to leave early in case your car breaks down, your train is late, or you run into bad traffic. This margin gives you space to take care of the situation and continue about your day without missing important plans or appointments.

Unsurprisingly, margins can also help reduce stress in our lives. If you start studying for an exam a week in advance, you will be less panicked about it than if you try to cram the night before. Stress can lead to poor decision-making, so reducing your stress can have positive ripple effects.

All this being said, most of us are busy and have many different responsibilities; we cannot build margins for everything. Margins could indeed be costly in some situations. There are two times when it makes sense to build margins: when the thing in question is important and when the cost of building the margin is reasonably low. For example, when I need to fly, I usually leave for the airport much earlier than necessary. This is a combination of an important event and a low cost: missing the plane could have major consequences, and because I can easily work while waiting for boarding, I can implement this margin with almost zero cost. Why risk it?

STREAKS OF GOOD LUCK

Now what about streaks of good luck? They happen too—hooray! I personally believe the best approach to such situations is humility. I need to make sure I do not get cocky or arrogant in good times as hubris can lead to mistakes. Instead, take advantage of the opportunities good luck can bring by building margins for Black Swans and bad times.

Borrowing again from finance literature, let's say times are good, and you are making good money. Great! While you are enjoying your wealth, it is a good idea to increase your contributions to your saving, and investing accounts. If you get a 20% raise or a significant bonus, for example, it is a good idea to save or invest at least half of the amount. As figure 1.2 demonstrates, this gives you an extra boost and helps to offset the times when things aren't so good.

This all might seem obvious and basic, but the truth is that many of us fail to follow these simple actions. Even intelligent business managers sometimes make big mistakes in this regard. This is one of the reasons many businesses fail every year: many of them simply do not implement margins in the good times to help them survive the bad times. So how can we get better at implementing margins?

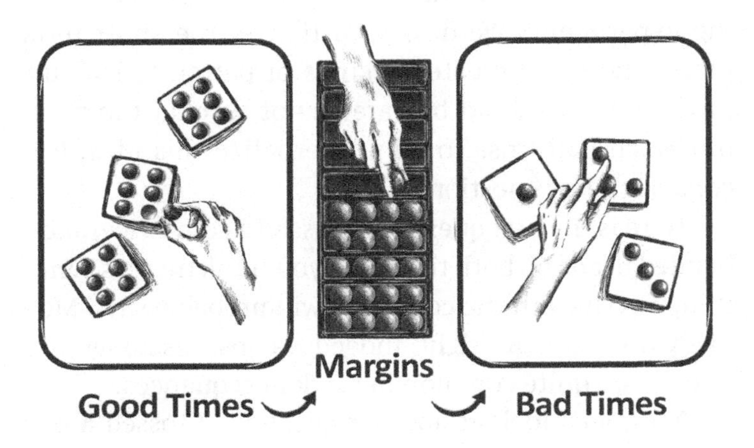

Figure 1.2. Taking advantage of lucky streaks. Increasing your margins during the good times can help offset the bad times.

One problem is that we might think building margins necessarily implies inefficiency. This is not true. For example, you could be very productive by being the kind of person who plans well and finishes most of their projects early.

One way to internalize the margin concept is to look at our past failures and develop contingencies to address those failures. Any time I have difficulty meeting a deadline, I know that it's because I have failed to build enough margin into my schedule. When another difficult deadline comes up, I look back and try to learn what I did wrong the last time so that I can prevent the same thing from happening again.

OUTCOME BIAS AND THE LAW OF SMALL NUMBERS

Here is another useful insight from our coin-tossing experiment: We discussed that in the short term, randomness can create all kinds of patterns. This implies that we should be careful not to read too much into such patterns. To help internalize this idea, let's consider a few questions.

Here is the first question: I tossed a coin twice, and it handed heads up both times. Do you think there is something wrong with the coin? You will probably say, "Most likely not." You are right. Indeed, we just discussed that streaks are quite common in random sequences.

Now, let's look at another question: I tossed a coin fifty times, and it landed heads up every time. What do you think now? You will probably say, "I am guessing this is a double-headed coin." Great; your intuition is spot-on.

What is the difference between the two cases? In the second case, you have a very large sample, so it makes sense for you to draw conclusions based on your observation. But in the first case, it could be very dangerous to draw conclusions from such a small sample. In the short term (i.e., when the sample size is small), it is usually difficult to separate luck and skill. Let's look at a few applications of this point.

Once, when I was at a party, I heard someone claim, "I don't believe in the healthy-living crap advertised by the media. My aunt, who had a very healthy lifestyle, died of cancer at the age of 55, while my uncle, who never exercised, smoked heavily, and was drunk all the time, is still alive at the age of 94." The flaw in his argument was that he could not conclude much from a sample size of two, the same way you could not infer much when you observed two heads in the coin toss example above.

This mistake is usually called belief in the "law of small numbers."[2] Note that this law of small numbers is not really a law; it is a fallacy. I was once burned by the law of small numbers. As a graduate student, I attended many conferences and workshops to present my work. I once slacked off on putting a good effort into practicing my presentation. To my surprise, it turned out to be one of my best presentations; everyone loved it. "Learning" from my experience, I showed up unprepared to the next event—and failed miserably.

My conclusion based on one sample was completely irrational. After that lucky talk, I came up with all kinds

2 The law of small numbers was explained by Amos Tversky and Daniel Kahneman in their 1971 paper, "Belief in the Law of Small Numbers," published in *Psychological Bulletin*, 76, no. 2.

of crazy theories to justify why unpreparedness is good for a speaker. But as I soon learned, my success in the first presentation was primarily due to luck.

In general, it would be a mistake to think a single good outcome implies that you have made a good decision. Psychologists refer to this mistake as the *outcome bias*. Again, the danger here is that we learn the wrong lesson when we evaluate a small number of decisions based on their outcome.

To further combat outcome bias, we should evaluate the quality of a decision based on the information available at the time it was made rather than the eventual outcome. We should consider alternative possible outcomes. For instance, if a decision yielded a positive result, we want to look for the factors that could have led to an unfavorable outcome. Conversely, if a decision resulted in a negative outcome, we want to consider the unpredictable factors that may have played a role.

A WARNING AND A MYSTERY

Let's end this short chapter with a warning and a mystery. First, the warning.

WARNING: THIS WAS A SIMPLIFIED VIEW

Admittedly, the above coin-tossing experiment provides a simplified view. Among other simplifications, it mostly ignores the magnitude of lucky or unlucky events, and it assumes lucky or unlucky events happen independently, i.e., they don't impact each other. None of these assumptions are accurate in real life.

(These issues will be discussed in later chapters.) Nevertheless, even this simplified coin toss example can provide some insights and lessons, and that's why we started here.

I would also like to emphasize the power of our simple coin-tossing process. Almost any complicated random process can be constructed mathematically using our simple coin toss example. Thus, this simple example can be thought of as a building block of much more sophisticated and more realistic random experiments we might face in real life.

This leads us to the mystery, which is related to the story of how I was first attracted to randomness and uncertainty.

THE MYSTERY OF RANDOM CODES

Suppose an engineer wants to design a car. She suggests the following method: select a random collection of car parts (wheels, engines, seats, etc.) and attach them to each other randomly. The designer claims this method will give you the best possible car. Do you take her claim seriously?

I am guessing you do not. I would agree with you—and that is why I was completely surprised when an instructor of mine made a similar claim during a college lecture I was attending. I was a third-year electrical engineering student attending a somewhat dull lecture on telecommunication systems. From my studies, I knew that since any form of data transmission could suffer from transmission errors, engineers need to design error control mechanisms (referred to as *error-correcting codes*).

Here is the weird part: the lecturer claimed that the best error-correcting codes can be designed by random construction. This was the part that shocked me. How can a random design be the best design? In fact, this method of random construction of error-correcting codes is a famous discovery by Claude Shannon, the father of information theory. I was excited by the power of such random codes, and this is indeed how my fascination with randomness and uncertainty started.

A few years later, I chose a modern version of such random codes as my doctoral research topic. In the years since, different versions of these random and pseudorandom codes have evolved to become new standards for communication devices. You have probably used them yourself when connecting to the internet, talking on your phone, and making video calls.

Now, why did I tell you this story? As it turns out, the construction of these random codes essentially boils down to a process not unlike our simple coin toss. The coin toss is, indeed, a very powerful operation.

In this book, we are concerned more with everyday applications of randomness than with technical or engineering applications. However, as we explore other practical applications of uncertainty in the next chapter, we will also be able to partially explain the mystery behind the power of random codes.

Indeed, exploiting randomness is a well-known strategy in computer science. Randomized algorithms are used extensively in data algorithms, which we all benefit from when we use the services of companies like Google, Facebook, and Amazon. A vital question for us is whether we can implement some of the ideas from randomized algorithms in our personal, business, and societal decisions. We will explore such questions in the upcoming chapters.

CHAPTER TAKEAWAYS

- It is useful to look at randomness as the lack of certainty. In this view, the concepts of uncertainty and randomness are practically the same.
- Due to randomness, we might all experience streaks of misfortune in our lives. Just knowing and expecting these streaks make them easier to deal with.
- Another useful point of view is looking at bad times as opportunities to improve and discover new opportunities.
- We tend to underestimate the lengths of our streaks of bad luck. They could, in fact, last much longer than we expect.
- We tend to overestimate the role of bad luck in our failures and underestimate the role of good luck in our success.
- Implementing margins, cushions, and redundancies is an effective way to deal with uncertainty and randomness. This also provides peace of mind, which can be priceless.
- We should build margins when the consequences of negative events could be significant and the cost or effort of implementing margins is reasonably small.

- Good luck streaks happen too. We should take advantage of them to increase our resilience and build capacity, for example, by reducing debt, increasing savings, and completing tasks ahead of schedule.
- Margins do not necessarily imply inefficiency. In fact, guarding against unpredictable events can keep us from losing efficiency.
- We can use our past failures to practice the habit of building margins into plans.
- The tendency to draw conclusions from small amounts of data is usually referred to as the law of small numbers. We should be careful not to read too much into short-term patterns, as such patterns might be the result of randomness.
- Outcome bias refers to the tendency to judge a decision by its outcome instead of basing it on the quality of the decision given what was known at that time. The danger here is that we might learn the wrong lessons, which can adversely impact our future decisions.

CHAPTER 2:

THE IMPACT OF LOW-IMPACT EVENTS

Ronald Read worked as a janitor and a gas station attendant. When he died in 2014, he had accumulated a fortune of almost $8 million.[3] Given his low salaries over the years, this is quite an impressive feat! What was his secret? Well, aside from being frugal, he benefited from two powerful mathematical concepts.

The first one is *exponential growth* (also called *compounding effect*), which you are probably familiar with. The second one is related to the convergence rules in probability, one example of which is the *law of large numbers*. This related concept is less commonly discussed, but as we will learn, it can have significant real-life implications.

In this chapter, we will strive to better understand the law of large numbers (LLN) and see how we can take advantage of this concept to make decisions in our daily lives that could lead to significant benefits over time.

3 Ronald Read's story was featured in Morgan Housel's informative book, *The Psychology of Money*.

A SIMPLE FORM OF THE LAW OF LARGE NUMBERS (LLN)

The simplest form of LLN can be explained using our coin. Let me ask you some easy questions first. Assuming the coin is fair, what is the probability of getting heads in a single toss? You say 50%. But what does it mean when we say the probability is 50%?

One way to answer this question is to explain that if I toss the coin a large number of times, we observe heads about 50% of the time. So, if you toss the coin 1,000 times and count the number of heads, the number will be close to 500. This is a simple form of LLN.

OK—so far, so good. Now, let's consider a trickier question: Can you give me an intuitive explanation of why LLN is true? Is there some invisible hand in the universe that ensures that in the long run, heads come up about 50% of the time? If you can't come up with an answer, don't feel bad; I often ask this question in my university probability classes, and even students who can solve complex probability problems often fail to provide a satisfying answer.

Before we go deeper into the chapter, I invite you to think about the answer. We know that the coin does not have memory, so no matter what we observe in the first 100 coin tosses, the 101st coin toss still has a 50% chance of resulting in heads. So how can these coin tosses somehow collude with each other so that by the end of the 1,000th coin toss, the percentage of heads is close to 50%?

I have found that an intuitive understanding of this mystery can help us improve our decision-making in our daily life, so we will start by developing this intuition.

We will then discuss practical applications of LLN and how we can benefit from this law.

One more note before we get started: it is helpful to contrast this chapter with the previous one. Here, we have a long-term point of view. In the previous chapter, we were mostly concerned with a short-term view. In the short term, we could observe streaks of heads or tails, and we discussed some practical implications of this fact. On the other hand, LLN enforces some regularity when the time span is large, i.e., when the number of coin tosses is large. As it turns out, we can immensely benefit from this regularity.

OK, let's get the fun started!

UNDERSTANDING THE LAW OF LARGE NUMBERS

Let me tell you a story. In the year 3025, two massive spaceships land on a planet. Each spaceship has about 1,000 passengers on board, and both groups choose this planet as their home. The group from the first spaceship is called Adventurers, and the group from the second spaceship is called Multipliers. Adventurers, not surprisingly, love adventures; they always choose to have small families so that they can maximize the number of adventures they have. On the other hand, the Multipliers love to have big families, so they don't go on as many adventures.

Initially, there are 1,000 people from each group on the planet. As the years pass, the number of Adventurers grows very slowly, so after 300 years, the initial group of 1,000 Adventurers reaches around 3,000. However, due to their higher growth rate, the number of Multipliers on the planet by that time has ballooned to about 1,000,000. Adventurers have become a rarity on the planet; more than 99% of the planet's residents are Multipliers.

Admittedly, I may not have a promising career as a science fiction writer, but I do have a point: as we will see, what happens on our imaginary planet very much resembles the law of large numbers. The key point here is that as each population grows, the portion of the population that consists of Multipliers increases; if you wait long enough, almost everyone on the planet will be a Multiplier. This is because, as shown in figure 2.1, the Multipliers are growing at a faster rate.

Now, let's give a probabilistic meaning to the situation 300 years after the spaceships land on the planet. If I select a person from this planet at random, the probability that I will select a Multiplier is higher than 99%. The same phenomenon happens in any population if one group in the population grows at a faster rate than the others: as figure 2.1 shows, after a long period of time, a randomly selected person will almost always be a person from the group with the higher growth rate.

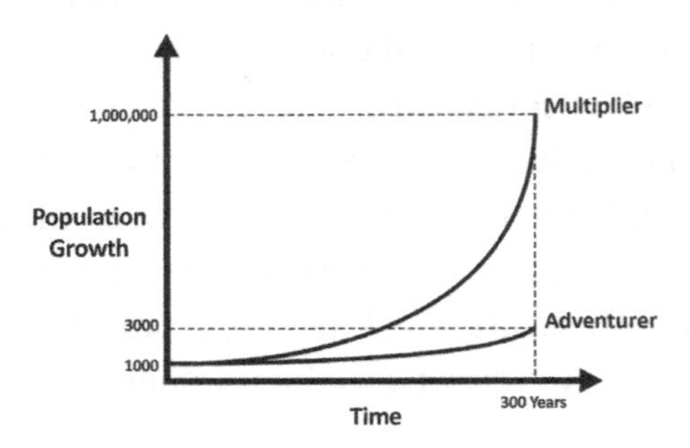

Figure 2.1. Population growth of Multipliers and Adventurers. As time passes, Multipliers dominate the planet due to higher growth rate.

As we will see, a similar phenomenon happens in our coin toss experiment and can help us better understand LLN.

In the next section, I will use the above analogy to provide the basis for an intuitive understanding of LLN. I'll try to keep the discussion intuitive, but admittedly, it will get a little bit technical. If you absolutely hate any kind of math, you have my permission to skip the following section and jump to the section titled "Towards Practical Interpretations of LLN."

TYPICAL SEQUENCES AND LLN

Before we attempt to develop an intuitive explanation of LLN, let's remember that we can compute the probability of events in our coin-tossing experiments simply by counting the possible number of desired *outcomes*, then dividing that number by the number of possible *sequences*. For example, if I toss a coin twice, what is the probability of observing exactly one heads? You can say there are four possible sequences: HH, HT, TH, and TT. In two of the sequences, there is exactly one heads, so the probability is 2/4, or 50%.

Now, let's return to the law of large numbers. LLN states that if we toss a coin many times, the cumulative proportion of heads will be close to 50%. What do we mean by "close to 50%"? Let's agree on a 5% margin of error; that is, the percentage of heads should be between 45 and 55%. We call sequences within this range *typical sequences*. That is, a typical sequence is a sequence where the proportion of heads is between 45 and 55%.

Let's test this out by tossing a coin 20 times. Based on our definition, if the number of observed heads is 9, 10, or 11, we have a *typical sequence*. But what are the actual chances of observing a typical sequence in this scenario?

As with the previous example, we can determine the answer by counting how many typical sequences exist for 20 coin tosses, then dividing that number by the total number of possible sequences that we could observe.[4] This calculation will give us the probability of observing a typical sequence when we toss a coin 20 times.

I'll save you the heavy lifting by telling you that if you do this for 20 tosses, you will find that about 50% of the sequences are typical. This means that if I toss a coin 20 times, there is about a 50% chance that the proportion of heads will be close to 50% (between 9 and 11 total heads) because the typical sequences in 20 tosses are about half of the total number of possible sequences.

Now, here is the interesting part: as we increase the number of coin tosses, the portion of typical sequences grows. If we look at the sequences of length 40, the portion of typical sequences grows to 57%. That is, if I toss a coin 40 times, there is a 57% chance that I observe a typical sequence of between 18 and 22 heads. For 80 coin tosses, the portion grows to 69%; for 200 coin tosses, to 86%, and for 500 coin tosses, it is 98%. See figure 2.2.

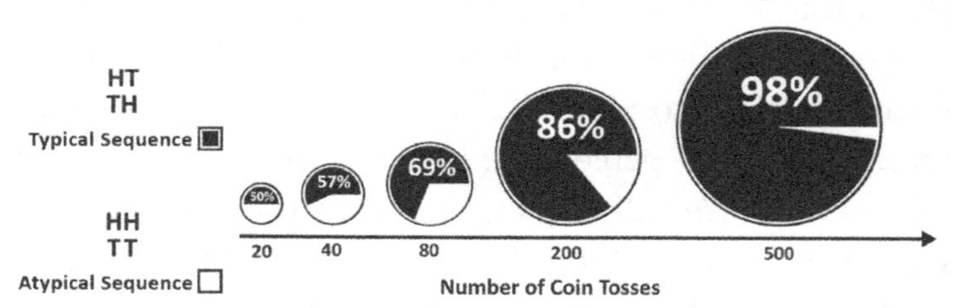

Figure 2.2. Typical and atypical sequences. The portion of typical sequences grows as the number of coin tosses grows. After 500 coin tosses, about 98% percent of sequences are typical (i.e., contain close to 50% heads).

4 In the two-coin-toss example, the typical sequence was the case in which we observed just one heads. In our four total possible sequences, there were two typical sequences.

You can see how portions increase as the number of coin tosses go up in the following chart:

Number of Coin Tosses	Number of Typical Sequences
20	50%
40	57%
80	69%
200	86%
500	98%

Just as how the Multiplier population grows at a faster rate than that of Adventurers, the number of typical sequences grows faster than the number of non-typical sequences. Thus, the relative portion of typical sequences grows as more coin tosses occur.

By the 1,000th coin toss, almost all the sequences are typical, just as after a few hundred years, almost everyone on our planet was a Multiplier. *This is the intuition behind LLN: there are many more ways to get close to 50% heads than any other percentage.* That is indeed one way to define the probability of observing heads. The probability of an event is related to the number of opportunities for that event to happen.

TOWARDS PRACTICAL INTERPRETATIONS OF LLN

As we saw above, when we toss a coin many times, the total number of observed heads is close to 50% of our total coin tosses. Now, let us look at a more general version of LLN and see how we can take advantage of it in real life.

LLN is concerned with the average or accumulated

result of many repetitions of experiments under specific conditions. It roughly states that if you perform many experiments and look at the total average result, you will see a result that is close to the true average or, as the statisticians call it, the *expected value*. Another way to interpret this is that in the long term, good and bad luck wash out, and one's true performance quality is observed.

For a practical application of LLN to be valid, three important conditions must be approximately satisfied: independence, low impact, and linearity.

1. The experiments must be more or less independent from each other. This condition holds for the coin toss example. Specifically, one coin toss does not affect another; a coin has no memory. This means that observing one heads does not change the probability of the next heads; that probability will still be 50%. This condition is known as the *independence assumption*.
2. Each individual experiment has a limited impact on the total sum. In other words, none of the individual experiments can dominate the final outcome. In the coin toss example, each coin toss can change the number of heads by one count at most. We call this condition the *low-impact assumption*.
3. The aggregate outcome must be obtained by simply adding the individual outcomes. We refer to this condition as the *linearity assumption*. In the coin toss example, any time we observe a heads, we increase the total sum by one, so we can say the aggregate outcome is obtained by adding the outcomes of individual coin tosses.

Consider a college student who completes many assignments, projects, and exams during her studies. Sometimes she performs better on an exam, maybe helped by a bit of good luck such as a quiet night and a lot of sleep the night before, and sometimes she performs worse, maybe hurt by a bit of bad luck such as a bad headache during the exam. Nevertheless, LLN states that in the long run, her GPA should be a good indicator of her overall talent and diligence regarding her coursework—assuming, of course, that no high-impact event significantly influences her performance (the low-impact assumption).

Put differently, the student's expected value represents her true level of talent and diligence. The GPA is the average outcome the student observes. LLN states that if the student takes a large number of courses, her GPA would be very close to her expected value.

Let's look at a different example where LLN may or may not hold. Can insurance companies take advantage of LLN? Suppose an insurance company computes the expected revenue from each customer over a certain time period and determines that the expected value per customer is $100. Let's assume LLN holds for this company. According to LLN, if the company has 100,000 customers, the total accumulated income will be around $10 million (100,000 times $100).

Remember, there are three conditions for LLN: independence, low impact, and linearity. If these conditions are not satisfied, the insurance company's total outcome could significantly deviate from the expected value of $10 million.

What might this deviation look like? Let's say the insurance company is insuring homes in an area with a high risk of an environmental disaster that could affect many homes simultaneously such as a flood or earthquake. In such a scenario, the independence assumption is not valid because homes are not affected independently. The possibility of this environmental disaster creates statistical dependence between homes.

Here's another example of a deviation: if there is no cap on the amount the insurance company can pay out to each customer, a single customer might become entitled to millions of dollars, which could significantly impact the whole outcome for the company. In this case, the low-impact assumption may not be valid. In practice, it has indeed been observed that a small number of claims account for a large percentage of total claims for many insurance companies. This is why insurance companies are usually careful not to apply LLN blindly in their business planning.

Now, here comes the fun part. How can we take advantage of LLN to increase the chances of achieving our goals?

LOW-IMPACT ACTIONS CAN BE HIGH IMPACT

One important lesson from LLN is the surprising cumulative impact of daily low-impact decisions. Remember, LLN states that in the long run, the accumulated impact of repeated actions is approximately the number of actions multiplied by the expected value. Thus, the larger the number of such actions, the higher the accumulated impact. We each make many decisions every day, so this number of actions could result in a large overall impact. To take advantage of LLN, we need to recognize the surprising potential impact of our daily low-impact decisions.

Consider two friends, John and Matt, both of whom wouldn't mind losing a few pounds. These two friends have almost the exact same lifestyle with only one small difference: John takes advantage of every small opportunity during the day to stay active and do a little exercise whenever he can, such as parking his car farther from buildings or taking the stairs, but Matt does not.

Let's simplify things and say that on average, John loses half a pound per week over a one-year period. Of course, this is not easily measurable in the short term due to the randomness in body weight fluctuations, but the effect will be visible by the end of the one-year period.[5] Through LLN, John will lose about 26 pounds by the end of the year, while Matt will weigh about the same as he did at the beginning of the year. John will observe a large difference in results because of a very small difference in lifestyle.

Due to the high media coverage of health-related topics, the impact of small daily habits on our overall health may be no huge surprise. However, due to LLN, the same phenomenon is true in almost all other areas of life. In other words, as shown in figure 2.3, repetitive, low-impact events can indeed become high impact over the long term. Unfortunately, because the results are not immediately visible, it is easy for us to underestimate the accumulating impact of our repetitive, low-impact actions.

5 We are ignoring the fact that body weight does not change linearly, but this fact is inconsequential to the point made here.

Figure 2.3. The accumulating impact of low-impact actions. Small, repetitive actions can add up and have a large cumulative effect.

PRACTICAL TOOLS TO TAKE ADVANTAGE OF LLN

It has been a long day. It is late, I feel tired, and I just want to collapse and possibly watch an NHL game. To be honest, I have a general tendency to be lazy (but don't tell anyone!), and I don't feel that I have the energy to do my running today. But thanks to a few tricks, I manage to do it.

There exists a large body of literature in fields such as psychology, economics, and business on how to improve our small daily decision-making to take advantage of the impact of low-impact actions due to LLN.[6] Below, I explain a few tricks that I have found most useful in my own life, from finding the motivation to exercise to improving my productivity.

1. THE POWER OF STARTING

The first trick I play on myself is the following: I tell myself that I will jog for just five minutes. It's as simple as that. This seems to be an effective trick, and I always fall

6 The Recommended Reading section at the end of this book includes a list of books on improving small daily habits.

for it. Most of the time, once I've started, I end up running for much more than five minutes. And on the very rare occasions that I only do five minutes, that time is still not nothing—remember LLN and its long-term effects.

Any time we know we should be doing something useful but we just don't feel like it, we can remind ourselves of the impact of LLN and tell ourselves, "I'll just do this for five minutes." If you commit to reading just three pages, writing just one page, or answering just two emails, you'll find it much easier to start than if you try to tackle everything at once. Thanks to the power of LLN, even that minimal amount of work is still helpful in the long run—and as a bonus, you usually end up doing more than you initially expected due to the momentum you obtain after starting.

2. REMOVING OBSTACLES

The second trick that helps me exercise when I don't feel like it is removing as many potential obstacles as possible between me and my run. We have a treadmill in the house, so all I need to do is get on the device; I cannot use the cold weather as a justification not to exercise. Knowing myself, I am sure that if I had to go through the trouble of getting ready, getting into the car, and driving to the gym, I would exercise much less. I am not denying the benefits of going to the gym; I am simply stating that making it easy to start my exercise by ensuring a minimum number of obstacles can be very useful, even if it is only used as backup for those days of lower motivation. Having a treadmill in my home is just one way I remove obstacles to exercising. It might be a good idea for us to think about how we can remove obstacles to other activities we deem important.

The reverse is also true; we might create obstacles to things we're tempted to do that are not good for us. For example, some people might leave their phone in a separate room so that they can focus on their work without being distracted by the temptation to check social media or other enticing apps.

3. CREATING INCENTIVES

The third trick that helps me do my exercise is creating incentives for myself. As a reward for exercising, I allow myself to listen to or watch my favorite programs while working out. I was using this idea for years before I found out there is a name for it: *temptation bundling*, a term coined by Katy Milkman, a professor at the Wharton School of the University of Pennsylvania.[7]

Creating incentives is another way we can take advantage of LLN. Such incentives give us additional motivation to complete tasks that we might not enjoy but are beneficial, thereby improving our average performance per day. As we know, this in turn could result in a large cumulative impact over time.

4. TASK ORDERING

Another trick to improve our average productivity is ordering our tasks in a strategic way. For example, I like to tackle the least enjoyable tasks on my plate in the morning, i.e., when I have the highest amount of energy. As I

7 Milkman's book *How to Change* includes many interesting tricks and strategies for achieving personal goals.

progress through the day and lose some of my willpower, I switch to the more enjoyable tasks. This helps keep me involved in my work and increases my productivity. Ordering my tasks with the least enjoyable tasks first is a way for me to *eat that frog* (to borrow a phrase coined by Brian Tracy in his bestselling book of the same name).

Obviously, different people react differently to a particular ordering of tasks, but each of us can probably improve our average productivity by cleverly ordering our daily tasks in the ways that work best for us.

5. COMMITMENT DEVICES

The final trick I find useful when I don't want to do something that is good for me is to lock myself into doing it. Every night, as soon as I feel I have had enough food for the day, I immediately floss and brush my teeth. This basically eliminates the danger that I will eat anything else that day. The secret is that I hate brushing my teeth; any enjoyment that I might get out of eating, say, ice cream is vanquished by the torture of having to brush again later that evening. This is an example of a commitment device, another well-known technique to improve our daily habits discussed.

It is easy to apply this technique to personal finance. For example, you can automate saving and investing a portion of your income. Paying the monthly mortgage on a home is another example of an opportunity for such automated savings. Think about what other commitment devices you can use in your life to keep yourself on track with your goals and reduce the likelihood that you'll skip important tasks.

BACK TO RONALD READ

At the beginning of this chapter, I mentioned the story of Ronald Read. It is easy to see why repetitive contributions to savings and investment accounts (a low-impact action), accompanied by compound interest, could help someone achieve big financial goals over a long period of time.

Interestingly, Mr. Read's story is a bit more complicated than that. In addition to the two factors I mentioned earlier, there is a third factor that benefited him. Can you guess what it is? I have already provided a clue somewhere in this chapter. We will discuss this in detail in later chapters. (I promise, I am not just being a jerk and creating suspense just to get you to read the rest of the book! I believe pondering this will help you internalize the concept.)

THE MYSTERY OF RANDOM CODES

In the previous chapter, I mentioned the mysterious power of random error-correcting codes. Specifically, I described how I was shocked when a college professor of mine claimed that the best error-correcting codes can be designed by a random construction. Now that we have understood LLN, we can partially resolve the mystery.

First, what do I mean by *code*? Here a code is simply a rule that assigns a sequence of zeros and ones to a given message. Now, you can think of this long sequence of zeros and ones as a sequence of heads and tails, like the one we discussed earlier in this chapter; let's say heads means a zero and tails means a one.

In other words, we can design the code randomly by tossing a coin. Now, a key insight by Claude Shannon was to use codes that consist of very long sequences of zeros and ones.

If the sequence is very long, good things happen, and we have some regularity. That is, as we discussed, any long, random sequence will be a typical sequence. The key point is that when you have a long sequence of heads or tails, many random fluctuations cancel each other, and you could have control over the outcome. This is a key factor in the power of random codes.

It turns out that there are other regularities or typicality properties at play that we did not discuss here. Of course, I do not get into the details here as it gets too technical (but is very mathematically beautiful!). Interested readers can refer to any of the excellent books on information theory, including *Elements of Information Theory* by Thomas Cover and Joy Thomas.

CHAPTER TAKEAWAYS

- A simple version of the law of large numbers (LLN) states that if you toss a coin many times, the number of observed heads will be close to 50%.
- Intuitively, LLN holds because there are many more sequences with close to 50% heads than all other possible sequences.
- Practically, LLN governs the aggregate impact of a large number of low-impact and relatively independent actions, where impacts are simply added to each other.
- Assuming that the independence, low-impact,

and linearity conditions are approximately satisfied, the overall cumulative impact of a large number of actions will be determined by the average or expected performance.

- An important implication would be that daily or repetitive low-impact actions are high impact in the long run. It is easy to underestimate the cumulative impact of such actions, a trap many of us fall into.
- The Power of Starting, Removing Obstacles, Creating Incentives, Task Ordering, and Commitment Devices are all techniques we can use to improve our daily habits.
- One benefit of understanding LLN is identifying when it does not hold. A completely different approach may be needed in such scenarios.

CHAPTER 3:

INFORMATION AND UNCERTAINTY

In 2018, after a long and careful analysis, I decided to purchase some Moderna stock for the price of $15 a share. In just a few years, my investment grew by more than 1,000%, just as I had predicted. In this chapter, I am going to show you how, in a few simple steps, you can duplicate my success and achieve your financial goals.

That is how I would tell the story if I were a charlatan. Here is the real story.

In 2018, I attended a Christmas party. I talked with a friend who worked for a then-unknown company called Moderna, and I decided to purchase some Moderna stock. I bought this stock randomly because some of my friends happened to work there, not because of any information I received from those friends regarding the company or any insight into the markets. I did not buy a lot of shares, so the 1,000% increase did not make me rich. I had no clue about the technology behind the company, nor did I know this technology could be useful in developing vaccines or that vaccines would soon be so necessary.

Thus, unfortunately, I am not going to reveal the secret to becoming rich. (Sorry.) Nevertheless, the concepts in this chapter will turn out to be fundamental in your decision-making and potentially useful in your investment decisions.

UNDERESTIMATED UNCERTAINTY

Let me ask you a question: How many times have you been conned or found yourself the subject of a scam? No matter what number you provide to answer this question, your answer is likely incorrect. Can you guess why?

I recently read the engaging book *The Confidence Game* by Maria Konnikova, which provides fascinating true stories about con artists. One interesting point she made is that the best cons are never discovered, so we never know how many times we have been conned without knowing it.

This is just one example of our inherent uncertainty. We humans generally hold a lot of beliefs and assumptions, and many of them are incorrect. Naturally, we do not know which of our beliefs are incorrect, and that is OK. It only becomes a problem when we act as if all of our beliefs are true representations of the world—in other words, when we underestimate our uncertainty and overestimate our information and knowledge.

As we will learn in this chapter, it can be advantageous to appreciate and even exploit such uncertainties in our decision-making. We'll also consider the idea that appreciating uncertainty does not mean lacking self-confidence. In fact, the opposite can be true. Uncertainty is a fundamental concept in decision-making, so the insight you'll develop in this chapter will be helpful not just throughout the rest of the book but in your everyday life.

UNCERTAINTY, INFORMATION, AND ENTROPY

Computers, smartphones, tablets, and other devices usually work in binary codes (i.e., zeros and ones). Who was the first person to introduce the applications of such binary codes? Who developed the theoretical foundation for communication systems such as cell phones and the internet? And who developed the measure for quantifying information and uncertainty that we are going to discuss next?

The answer to all of the above questions is Claude Shannon. If I had to choose *the* person of the twentieth century (though nobody asked me to do so, and I am obviously biased), I would consider it a toss-up between Claude Shannon or Diego Maradona. Not to ignore Pelé's extraordinary talent, but I would go with Maradona as he had a more colorful personality, though I don't necessarily agree with his political views!

Anyway, back to Shannon. Shannon introduced a metric for measuring and quantifying uncertainty. He called this measure *entropy* because it is related to the entropy concept used in physics. Before we move on, let's look briefly at how entropy can quantify information and uncertainty. My goal here is not to provide a comprehensive definition of this term, as that would be outside the scope of this book, but rather to help you develop some intuition about entropy so that you can apply this important concept practically. As this intuition is best developed through examples, let's look at some examples of entropy that will help us better understand how it relates to randomness and uncertainty in our lives.

WHAT IS INFORMATION?

You are probably familiar with the game of Twenty Questions: I choose an object—say, a person—and you are supposed to guess the answer by sequentially asking only binary questions (questions that can be answered with a yes or no). For example, both "Is the person alive?" and "Is the person fictional?" would be acceptable questions. Now, what do you think is a good general strategy to use if you are the person asking the questions?

Here is a good strategy: at each stage of the game, you should try to ask questions where the probability of *yes* is about 50% so that *yes* or *no* are almost equally likely answers. Let's call such questions *balanced questions*. For example, leaving gender bias aside for the moment, "Is the person male?" is a balanced question as the answer can only be yes or no, and either would have a probability of about 50%. On the other hand, a question like "Is the person Ariana Grande?" is probably not good to ask at the beginning stages of the game as it is too specific, and the probability of a *yes* response is far from 50%.

As the game progresses, the majority of potential persons are eliminated, and the balanced questions become more specific. Indeed, even the Ariana Grande question might become balanced in the final stages of the game if you have narrowed down the answer to only a few remaining people.

MEASURING INFORMATION AND UNCERTAINTY

Here is a more interesting question: Why is asking balanced questions a good technique when playing Twenty Questions? Because their answers reveal the highest possible amount of information on average. We can measure an amount of information using entropy as a measure of average information. The unit usually used to measure entropy is called the *binary digit* or *bit*.

Roughly speaking, one bit is the amount of information contained in a variable that is equally likely to be zero or one. However, measuring information is a much more general concept that goes beyond variables with equally likely outcomes. We can measure the information contained in almost any message. To do so, let's first discuss why information and uncertainty can be both measured using the same metric, i.e., entropy.

When we gain information about an event, our uncertainty about that event is reduced; this is why information and uncertainty are really just two sides of the same coin. In other words, because uncertainty is the lack of information, we can use entropy to measure both information and uncertainty. If I gain two bits of information about an event, my uncertainty about that event is reduced by two bits.

Thus, we can think about entropy in two ways:

1. Entropy is the amount of information that we *lack* about a question (i.e., our uncertainty about the question).
2. Entropy is the amount of information we *obtain* when we receive the answer to the question.

Consider a question with a binary outcome: Will the sun rise tomorrow? We consider this a binary question since it is a *yes* or *no* question: the sun either will or will not rise tomorrow. How much uncertainty do you have about the answer? You would likely say around zero bits since this event has a probability close to 100%. We are almost sure it is going to happen, so we have close to zero uncertainty about this event.

Next, consider the following question: Will you meet an alien tomorrow? How much uncertainty do you have about this question? You might again say around zero, as this event has a probability close to 0%—we are almost sure it is not going to happen—so again, our uncertainty about this question is near zero.

So far, so good. We agree that we have almost no uncertainty about binary cases with probabilities close to 100% or 0%. But as the probability of the event moves closer to 50%, our uncertainty is increased. That is, we are less able to predict the outcome of such events. We have the maximum uncertainty about an experiment with a binary outcome when its probability is 50%. This is an important point and the clue to the Twenty Questions game strategy.

Remember that the information you gain when you are given the answer to a question is equal to the uncertainty you have about that question. That is why balanced questions give you the highest amount of information: you have the maximum amount of uncertainty about an answer that has a 50% probability.

SHANNON ENTROPY

Claude Shannon provided a precise measure for evaluating the quantity of information and uncertainty. For binary outcomes, the quantity of uncertainty is zero for events with a probability of 0% and 100%, and it is maximized at 50%. This maximum is equal to one bit, which is also equal to the amount of uncertainty that we have about a binary event with a probability of 50%. In other words, we get one bit of information when a choice between two equally likely outcomes is revealed.

Figure 3.1 shows the mathematical function behind this concept.

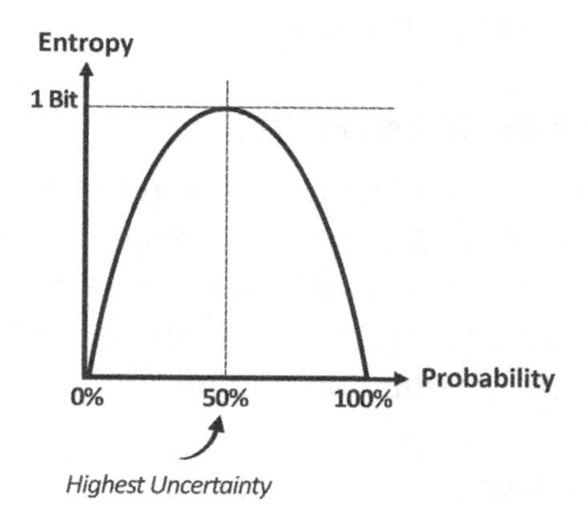

Figure 3.1: Binary entropy function. The quantity of uncertainty for events with a 0% or 100% probability is zero, and the maximum uncertainty occurs at a 50% probability.

This measure of uncertainty is called *information entropy*, *Shannon entropy*, or simply *entropy*. For our purpose here, we need not concern ourselves with its exact mathematical function. It is enough to know that entropy is higher when the possible outcomes are closer to being equally likely. For binary outcomes, *equally likely* means when each outcome has a probability close to 50%. Similarly, if you have three possible outcomes, the maximum entropy (i.e., the maximum uncertainty) occurs when we are indifferent between the outcomes; that is, when each has a probability close to 33%. In general, if there are N potential outcomes, the highest entropy is achieved when we are indifferent to the N outcomes; that is, when each outcome has a probability of 1/N.

If you would like to dig deeper into the concept of entropy, Appendix A provides some intuitive discussion about this concept. There we discuss how entropy can be thought of as the "average surprise" when you receive the answer to a question.

SUMMARY OF ENTROPY

Before moving on, let's check our intuitive understanding of these concepts. In the previous chapters, we defined *randomness* as uncertainty. In this chapter, we mentioned that *uncertainty* is the lack of information. Therefore, information and uncertainty can be quantified using the same measure. One such measure is called entropy.

Assuming N potential outcomes, the highest uncertainty occurs when we are indifferent about the N outcomes; that is, when each outcome has a probability of 1/N. In this case, we say we have a *uniform probability distribution*. In general, the higher the uncertainty, the more uniform the distribution. This is just another way of saying that as randomness increases, uncertainty also increases. In probability theory, we say that entropy is a measure of the evenness of the distribution.

Now, let's discuss how these concepts can be used in practical decision-making beyond games of Twenty Questions.

EXAMPLE: PRIVACY AS UNCERTAINTY

The digital world provides us with many benefits. Websites and apps provide personalized services tailored to our specific needs and tastes: movie recommendations, product suggestions, personalized search results, targeted ads, and many more. Now, the reason that we can enjoy these personalized services is that websites, apps, and devices are constantly collecting information from us.

Our searches, likes, posts, physical locations, and more are being constantly monitored. In theory, your phone and the apps on it could potentially listen to your conversations to further collect information from you. This collected information is then used to provide the personalized services you enjoy. Hence there is a trade-off: The more information companies collect from us, the more data these companies have about us, and the more personalized and potentially better experience we could have while using internet-based services.

On the other hand, some people might not be comfortable with the level of personal information that is collected and kept about them. After all, equipped with data and powerful machine learning algorithms, companies have the potential to learn deeply personal information about us. You might have heard the old story about Target discovering the pregnancy of a teenager before anyone else knew about it. This, of course, was just the tip of the iceberg.

HOW CAN WE ENSURE OR IMPROVE OUR PRIVACY?

You might be wondering why I am suddenly talking about privacy. The answer is that fundamentally, enhancing your privacy means that other parties have less information about you—which means they have more uncertainty. Thus, privacy is a good example to use when talking about entropy and uncertainty.

So what can you do if you would like to improve your privacy? Remember, uncertainty and randomness are the same thing, so you can use randomness to improve your privacy.

Let's say you are using a restaurant recommendation app that accesses your current location, then recommends restaurants to you based on that location, your preferences, and other factors. However, most apps do not need to know your exact location in order to do their job. For example, why does an app (and potentially the employees at the app's company) need to know that you are at a doctor's office right now when you just want to search for restaurants in the neighborhood? This kind of data examination could potentially leak information about your medical conditions.

One solution for increasing privacy is to increase uncertainty (i.e., entropy) by providing an intentionally imprecise location. This can be done by either setting the app to receive only an approximate region or randomly changing your location by a small amount and reporting the distorted location to the app. Both methods achieve essentially the same goal: introducing more uncertainty into your data. When your location has been randomly distorted, the app only knows your approximate region.

Indeed, most smartphones provide these privacy options to their users. They are not usually chosen by default, so you'll likely need to adjust your phone's privacy settings. Of course, providing an approximate location might adversely affect the functionality of some apps depending on what you use them for. Some years ago, with the help of our undergraduate students, my collaborators and I designed an application that automatically detected the location accuracy each specific app actually needed to function, then adjusted the levels of random distortion accordingly before reporting the location to each app.

This idea of increasing randomness—and hence privacy—can be used in many contexts. For example, you might install a browser plug-in that visits random websites in the background while you surf. These random sites could overwhelm your own true web traffic, preventing anyone from learning too much about your real web activity.

My goal here is to give examples of practical usages of the entropy concept. It is not to provide a thorough coverage of the topic of privacy; the topic of privacy is too big to cover in a small section. That said, I will end this section by providing some general privacy tips. If you are concerned about your digital privacy, you might want to try the following:

- Adjust the privacy settings on your devices, social media, and other apps and websites. Turn off your apps' access to your location, contacts, and other information unless it is essential.
- Further limit location access by allowing apps to detect your location only while they are in use, and set them to detect only your approximate location. This setting should be sufficient to allow many apps to function as intended.
- Choose options that prevent apps from running in the background.
- Consider deleting old posts (this can usually be done automatically), and limit the information you reveal on social media.
- Change your social media settings so that your activity is visible only to people you know.

The discussion above only scratches the surface of the topic of privacy. As technology evolves very fast in this area, it might be a good idea to spend some time every few years educating ourselves about this topic.

MINIMUM ASSUMPTION APPROACH

Now, let's discuss how we can potentially use the concepts of uncertainty and entropy in decision-making.

We mentioned that we tend to underestimate the uncertainty of each situation and often make assumptions that are not necessarily true. Naturally, we do not know which of our assumptions are false.

A general approach to this conundrum could be to make decisions in such a way that they rely on the minimum number of assumptions. Such decisions would be more robust to random or unexpected events. Let's refer to this general decision-making approach as the *minimum assumption approach* (MAA). As we will see throughout the book, the MAA could be used in different ways and contexts to improve the robustness of our decision-making.

Here is one example of how we might apply the MAA to our daily lives. Since we often underestimate our uncertainty, to account for our underestimation, it might make sense to assume a higher level of uncertainty when making a decision. Since entropy is a measure of uncertainty, increasing entropy means assuming higher uncertainty. This method is known as the *maximum entropy approach* pioneered by E. T. Jaynes.

In this chapter, we are less interested in mathematical details and more interested in applying the basic idea in our decision-making. As mentioned, we can think of the maximum entropy idea as one way to apply of our minimum assumption approach (MAA). So to keep things simpler, we simply use the MAA as a general term, by which we aim at making decisions that rely on the fewest possible assumptions. Now, let's look at one application of this idea in finance.

APPLICATION TO FINANCE: THE RELAXED 1/N RULE

Suppose that as part of your investment plans, you have allocated a few thousand dollars to invest in three promising financial assets—let's call them A, B, and C. How would you allocate your money among these three assets? Well, you might start by considering your existing opinions about the quality of these assets. For example, you might rank A better than B and B better than C in terms of your estimated return for each. Therefore, you might decide to allocate 80% of the money to A, 20% to B, and nothing to C.

Now, let us look at the situation from the perspective of maximum entropy or uncertainty (or, more generally, our MAA). If you want to make the minimum number of prior assumptions about the situation, you might proceed as follows.

To get away from any previous assumptions you may have had about these assets, you choose to become indifferent about them. Thus, you allocate one third of your allocated funds to A, one third to B, and one third to C. This is known in finance as the 1/N rule. This rule simply states that if you have N assets, you allocate your money equally between them (1/N for each asset), resulting in a uniform allocation.

Naturally, you might not be ready to throw away all of your assumptions and apply a maximum uncertainty approach—but you can still use the MAA idea without completely disregarding your prior opinions. For example, you can make your distribution more uniform than your original allocation by giving 50% to A, 30% to B, and 20% to C. Therefore, you are still using your original assumption that A is preferable to B and B is preferable to C, but your allocation of funds is closer to the uniform distribution suggested by the maximum uncertainty approach. In this way, you are reducing rather than negating the weight of your original prior assumptions. Let's refer to this "middle ground" approach as the *relaxed 1/N rule* as shown in Figure 3.2.

In sum, regardless of what we may *think* we can expect as a return on our investments, financial assets are usually highly unpredictable. Therefore, allocating funds in a relatively uniform way is more robust than a highly nonuniform allocation. In addition to the minimum assumption approach, there are other mathematical arguments in favor of the (relaxed) 1/N rule, which we will discuss later in this book.

You can apply the MAA to diversify your investment among different asset classes such as stocks, bonds, and real estate. Both the 1/N rule and the relaxed version

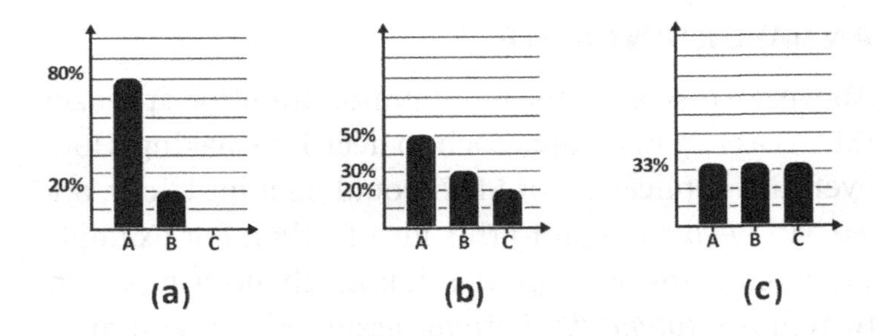

Figure 3.2. Three possible allocations of funds.

(a) No MAA: reflects the maximum reliance on assumptions.

(b) The relaxed 1/N rule: reduces the reliance on assumptions, moves toward higher uncertainty in prior assumptions, and is more robust compared to (a).

(c) The extreme MAA: reflects the minimum reliance on prior assumptions.

discussed above simply suggest that it might be a good idea to invest in several categories of investments. Of course, the assumption here is that you have already done some sifting to select your potential options. The 1/N rule does not necessarily suggest you should invest in your cousin Joe's next crazy business venture.

When investing within the stock market, one way to implement an approximation of the 1/N rule is to buy index funds, which are essentially samples of everything going on in the stock market. Using index funds, we can obtain the average performance of the market—meaning we can get the same returns on our investments as many professional investors.

Intriguingly, the concept of entropy turns out to be an important notion when it comes to investment. For example, entropy is related to what is often referred to as *log-optimal* or *Kelly growth-optimal* portfolios. We will return often to investment questions in future chapters.

AN IMPORTANT NOTE!

Above, we discussed the minimum assumption approach (MAA) as a general approach to decision-making. However, the application of MAA could be a bit tricky, and we will need to dig into this idea further. For example, when removing assumptions, it is much more important to remove *potentially harmful* assumptions. Perhaps a better name would be the *minimum potentially harmful assumption approach* (MPHAA)—but that name would be too long, so we'll stick with MAA.

This means that the MAA approach does not always necessarily mean moving toward more uniform prior assumptions, i.e., equally likely outcomes. This is especially important in risk management, which will be discussed in future chapters. It is also worth noting that entropy can quantify only a specific kind of uncertainty. For example, it cannot capture what are usually referred to as "unknown unknowns," e.g., risks that we are completely unaware of.

A FEW REMARKS AND MY BUSINESS IDEA

I would like to say a few things before we move on.

First, I am not a professional investor, so none of what I discuss in this book should be considered investment advice. These discussions simply look at problems, including examples from the world of investment, through the lens of uncertainty.

Second, for full disclosure, I use a version of the 1/N rule for my own stock investments. I tend to buy a lot of individual stocks. So why don't I just buy index funds as mentioned above? The main reason is that I enjoy picking these stocks randomly, which makes investing feel like a game to me. (A minor reason for buying individual stocks is that randomly picking stocks seems to be a good way for me to avoid any kind of fees.) I should stress that I spend less than 10 minutes per month on my stock investments. I also apply the relaxed 1/N rule when considering categories of assets by, for example, always keeping a certain percentage of my money in cash or cash equivalents.

Third, while we can think of playing the stock market as a form of gambling, there are some notable differences, including that the stock market has a more favorable legal structure, and the odds of winning are usually better than gambling. Some years ago, I had a business idea: a financial institution could set up a platform with an interface very similar to a slot machine. Then, whenever you "pull" the arm, you get matched to a trade. Using complex financial products, the institution could make the probability distribution of winnings somewhat similar to gambling but, hopefully, with better odds. People may be interested in such a service because they could satisfy their gambling desires and at the same time receive a better financial reward. Further, the institution could avoid any legal issues involved with gambling since the service is, in fact, merely an investment tool. I actually met with a person from my university's intellectual office who politely informed me that this was a dumb idea.

CONFIDENTLY UNCERTAIN

By now, we have discussed some advantages of appreciating uncertainty and its applications in decision-making using versions of the MAA. But are there any disadvantages? You might protest that admitting uncertainty could make you look less confident and put you at a disadvantage compared to those who appear very certain in their opinions. After all, who votes for a politician who says, "I am 65% confident that if we follow my plan, we will have a good economy next year"?

Well, I believe we can be both uncertain and confident at the same time. Julia Galef provides an interesting discussion on this in her excellent book, *The*

Scout Mindset. To see why confidence and uncertainty are not mutually exclusive, we can consider a few points (most of which are adapted from Galef's book):

First, perceived confidence does not always depend on the content of the message. Instead, it often depends on confident behavior: posture, tone of voice, calmness, and, of course, confident language. Thus, one can confidently argue why uncertainty is justified in a specific case and remind one's audience that claiming to offer absolute certainty is often a sign of charlatanism.

Second, by accepting uncertainty, one can provide a more comprehensive plan of action that will account for many possible outcomes. A company might provide a multiyear warranty on their product. At its core, this is an admission that the product might fail (that is, they are not certain that the product *won't* fail), but if it does, they are prepared to make their customers happy by replacing the failed product. I don't know about you, but I would rather buy from this company than from a company that does not provide a good warranty and instead claims—however confidently—that their product will never fail.

Third, by quantifying uncertainty in an honest and appropriate way, one can indicate their expertise on the matter. One way to do this is by providing statistical evidence. For example, a doctor might tell a patient that based on the available statistics from reputable sources, the chance of an operation's success is 80%. If the doctor conveys this message with confidence, the patient is likely to interpret it as expertise rather than lack of confidence.

CHAPTER TAKEAWAYS

- We usually underestimate our uncertainty and overestimate our knowledge. It's likely that many of our assumptions are false, but we don't know which. Even so, we usually act as if our assumptions are a true representation of the world.
- In unpredictable environments such as financial markets, it is usually beneficial to use our inherent uncertainty to guide our decision-making.
- When we are uncertain about the outcome of an experiment, we call it a random experiment. Therefore, the word *uncertainty* as we use it in this book refers to the level of randomness.
- Entropy is a measure of uncertainty. Entropy is usually maximized (i.e., we have the highest uncertainty) when we are totally indifferent about the potential outcomes, meaning that all outcomes are equally likely.
- The minimum assumption approach (MAA) is a general approach to decision-making that encourages us to make our decisions with the least possible number of assumptions.
- One way to interpret the MAA is the 1/N rule in finance, which suggests that we should divide our investment equally among assets.
- The relaxed 1/N rule is a less strict version of 1/N; it recommends that we move our allocation of funds closer to a uniform distribution but not necessarily in a perfectly uniform distribution. In other words, it is the middle ground between the ultimate MAA and an allocation based entirely on our assumptions.

- Some assumptions are potentially more harmful than others. Thus, a better way to refer to the MAA would be the *minimum potentially harmful assumption approach*. This means that the MAA approach does not always mean moving toward a uniform distribution, i.e., maximum entropy.
- Entropy can quantify only a specific kind of uncertainty. It cannot capture "unknown unknowns."
- Our devices, apps, and websites are constantly collecting data from us that could reveal deeply personal information.
- Improving our privacy means increasing others' uncertainty about our data, so we can increase our privacy by increasing randomness. This can be done by using settings and applications that report approximate versions of our location, visit random websites to obscure our browser history, and so on.
- We can further improve our privacy by adjusting the privacy settings on our devices, social media, and other apps; limiting the information we reveal on social media; and deleting old posts.
- There is a trade-off between privacy and the utility of our apps: the less information our apps and devices have about us, the less potentially personalized service they can provide.
- We can be both confident and uncertain. Helpful techniques to achieve this include behaving in a confident way (tone, posture, language, etc.), making comprehensive plans that address multiple contingencies, and quantifying uncertainty.

CHAPTER 4: RISK, ENTREPRENEURSHIP, AND HARM AVOIDANCE

It is the summer of 1990; I am 12 years old and watching a lousy FIFA World Cup game between Brazil and Scotland. It is about midnight local time, and I am the only one in the living room. Then, around the middle of the game, something strange happens. It takes a second for me to understand what is going on. The building is shaking, and it feels like the entire four-story structure will soon collapse. My family lives on the third floor, so if it did collapse, there would be no way to escape.

It would turn out that this was an enormous and tragic earthquake that killed about 40,000 people and injured close to 100,000 more. The epicenter of the earthquake was not very close to where I lived, so we survived.

I learned a few lessons from this event. First, the group-stage games in the World Cup usually suck. The Brazil–Scotland game was no exception: a boring match with one measly goal near the end. The second lesson is that even though they're boring, those group-stage games might still be worth watching; as it happens, the Brazil–Scotland game saved thousands of lives that night. How? People stayed up late to watch the game, meaning many who might otherwise have been asleep were able to escape their homes before their buildings collapsed. I vividly remember that this was one of the few comforting thoughts that went through my mind in the aftermath of the event.

However, the most important lesson I learned was that big events can appear out of nowhere and change our lives entirely. In just minutes, tens of thousands of people died, and many more were injured or lost their loved ones. The impact of these big events does not obey the law of large numbers (LLN) that we discussed in previous chapters, so we need a completely different approach to dealing with them.

In this chapter, we continue with the uncertainty framework discussed in the previous chapter. We first revisit low-impact (safe) events, then discuss negative high-impact (harmful) events through the lens of uncertainty. We also discuss important topics such as randomizing, risk-taking, entrepreneurship, and avoiding high-impact negative events.

A quick note before we start: in this book, the word *risk* is used in a broad way and simply means any kind of threat or danger. It refers to any situation where we are exposed to the possibility of loss or injury. When we talk about risk-taking, we simply mean taking any action that might result in substantial harm.

TWO EASY QUESTIONS

Before we dig in, let me pose two questions for you about two different scenarios; we'll call them gamble A and gamble B. The rest of this chapter will make the most sense if you take the time to answer each question before continuing.

Gamble A: You will either lose $100 or win $100. The probability that you win is 60%, so the probability that you lose is 40%. Would you take the gamble?

You might argue as follows: Although $100 is a considerable sum of money, it will not have a significant impact on my finances over the long run. In other words, the impact of this gamble can be aggregated into thousands of other independent financial decisions that I will make over the long term. Therefore, I can use the law of large numbers (LLN) to inform my decision. This means that I should look at the average or expected value of this gamble.

The expected return here is positive: if I were to play this game many times, I would win 60% of the time and lose 40% of the time. Thus, the expected return per game is (60% × $100) – (40% × $100), which comes out to be $20. This means that over time, I can expect an average return of $20 per game. Given the positive expected return, I take the gamble.

Now, let's look at gamble B.

Gamble B: You will either lose $1 million or win $1 million. The probability that you win is 60%, so the probability that you lose is 40%. The conditions here are similar to the first question with one difference: now, $1 million is at stake. Let's assume your entire net worth is less than $1 million. Would you take the gamble?

You might argue as follows: Although this game has a positive expected return, it is just too risky. I have a 60% chance of becoming a millionaire, but I have a 40% chance of complete financial ruin. Clearly, this is a high-impact event, and LLN does not apply here. Given the high risks, I decline the gamble.

Awesome! It seems we have solved the decision-making dilemma for humankind: For low-impact decisions, we should always choose the option with the highest average or expected return. For high-impact decisions, we should always pay close attention to potential loss and try to avoid options with the potential for significant harm. Hooray!

Of course, as I'm sure you've already deduced, real life tends to be more complicated than that. This is what we will examine next.

PROGRESSING TO TOUGHER QUESTIONS

The above questions are relatively easy to answer. But why is that so? One reason is that financial decisions are easier to quantify than decisions about other aspects of life. However, the main reason is that the problem is clearly defined, and all of the potential outcomes and their probabilities are known. Moreover, there are only two options—taking the gamble or declining it—and each option has well-defined results with known payoffs.

However, most of the personal and societal decisions we must make are not so clean and well-defined. Say that you are debating whether to start a restaurant business. You do some research and find out that the success rate of restaurants in your area is about 30%. While this could be a starting point for your decision-making, there are numerous other factors that you could and should consider in your analysis, including the effort required, the resulting stress, and the experience you'd gain that could help you in future ventures even if your first attempt fails. How would you quantify those factors? The range of potential outcomes is also wide, from losing all of your savings to becoming the owner of a successful national restaurant chain. There are many other factors that make this decision much more complicated than the simple gamble decisions above.

In the rest of this chapter, we will further examine high-impact and low-impact decisions and consider how our uncertainty approach can potentially help us in the decision-making process.

POTENTIAL HARM: A WAY TO CATEGORIZE EVENTS

Let's first be clear what we mean by *low impact* and *high impact*. The key is to look at the *potential harm* associated with a decision or an event. For the purpose of this book, if there is a nonnegligible chance of a catastrophic outcome, let's put it in the *harmful* (high-impact) category. Otherwise, if the chance of catastrophe is negligible, we place it in the *safe* (low-impact) category.

Note that there is always a chance of a catastrophe in anything we do. Even something as simple as leaving the house to go grocery shopping carries the chance of getting into a terrible accident. We all accept such risks every day and consider them small. In fact, to be effective at completing our daily tasks, we need to accept such risks. Outside of taking standard precautions like being watchful when crossing the street, there is not much we can do to mitigate them.

With that in mind, let's first discuss low-impact (safe) decisions and events.

LOW-IMPACT DECISIONS AND EVENTS

In earlier chapters, we've mentioned that the accumulating impact of independent low-impact decisions is usually governed by LLN. We discussed that repetitive, everyday low-impact actions can be high-impact in the long run, but that it is easy to underestimate the cumulative impact of such actions. We also discussed some techniques that might help us take advantage of LLN to improve our daily habits.

Our previous discussion on these low-impact events mostly focused on scenarios in which we more or less knew which options were the good ones. I know it is better for me to exercise than to sit on the couch; that is obvious. Now, from the perspective of uncertainty, let's discuss low-impact decisions where the best option is not so clear. How should we approach these scenarios when they arise? We'll start with the simpler topic of working out the cost of our decisions, then move toward the more profound topics of risk-taking, luck, and skill.

UNCERTAINTY AND DECISION COST

So far, we have ignored one aspect of decision-making: the cost of the decision-making process. By *cost*, I mean the time, mental energy, and resulting stress involved in deciding what to do in any given situation. The thing about small decisions is that we make many of them every day, and the accumulated decision cost could be large. From previous discussions, we know that due to unavoidable uncertainty, it is not always possible to determine the best option anyway. Therefore, instead of seeking perfection, we can at least reduce the cost of our decisions.

Suppose I want to buy five T-shirts. I could walk around the mall, look at all the brands of shirts available, write down the pros and cons of each, and compare them all. But that would be a waste of time. Instead, I could do what is called *satisficing*, a combination of "satisfying" and "sufficing" introduced by political scientist Herbert Simon. The idea is that you set requirements for your choices before beginning your search. In my hunt for a T-shirt, those requirements might be the right size, a color I like, and a cost of under $20 each. Now, when I go to the mall, I buy shirts that fit those criteria as soon as I find them, and I stop shopping when I reach five shirts. The goal of satisficing is to spend only the time and energy necessary to find something that is *good enough*. It is important to note that satisficing only works for situations where the potential for harm is very limited.

Research suggests that people who satisfice are happier with their lives than those who try to maximize their options. Satisficers have more time and energy to spend on more important things, and they tend to suffer less frequently from buyer's remorse; they don't, for example, waste time wishing they had bought the other shirt they were considering, because there was no other shirt. Satisficing might not achieve the exact maximum expected value or utility, but the time and effort saved are invaluable. There is so much randomness and uncertainty in the world (not to mention T-shirts) that no one can pick the perfect option every single time. Thus, our appreciation of uncertainty gives us a powerful justification for satisficing.

To summarize, satisficing could be a good option when (1) the decision has low stakes, and (2) there is high uncertainty.

UTILIZING RANDOMNESS AND RISK-TAKING

The uncertainty mindset can also help us make low-harm decisions in a much more fundamental and powerful way: by making use of the surprising power of randomness. Have you ever wondered how companies that work with a gigantic amount of data manage to process such data efficiently? For example, how can a search engine know if it has already processed a given web page?

Randomness is a powerful tool such companies have at their disposal. Indeed, there is an entire field in computer science called *randomized algorithms*. This field has influenced the development of many services that we enjoy daily. For example, the cryptographic methods used in secure communication have benefited greatly from probabilistic algorithms. Also, remember that in the previous chapter, we discussed how randomization is helpful in preserving our privacy.

OK, so randomness is very powerful, and computer scientists have used it extensively. Now, we need to understand how we can use this power in our personal or professional decision-making. However, allowing randomness into our decision-making can often feel counterintuitive. We face a set of obstacles:

1. We tend to underestimate the power and benefits of randomness in life and business. Indeed, we usually work too hard to reduce randomness and uncertainty, thereby depriving ourselves of their benefits.
2. We tend to confuse a randomized strategy with a lack of strategy.
3. Some of us are too afraid of small losses or failures. In order to benefit from randomness, we need to be comfortable with incurring small failures.
4. The payoffs from randomized strategies occur at random, and there could be a long delay between following a randomized strategy and observing the payoff. This makes many of us uncomfortable.

All of these factors work together to make randomization one of the least utilized tools in decision-making. However, incorporating randomness into our decision-making has the potential for huge payoffs and allows for creativity that might otherwise not be possible. My personal takeaway is that when the harm is limited, it can benefit us to purposefully allocate a portion of our time to exploring and trying new and random things.

For example, we could decide that up to 20% of the time, we will engage in the following actions:

- Trying random unfamiliar things
- Meeting people from groups we do not usually encounter
- Playing with random or unorthodox ideas in work or business
- Giving ourselves a chance to challenge our regular routines

While the potential harm from each of these actions is limited, the positive payoffs could potentially be large. A key idea here is that these random behaviors can lead to unknown opportunities. Randomness is probably one of the strongest forces behind innovation and creativity.

I mentioned in the introduction that everything I present in this book has personally benefited me, so before we proceed, let me tell you the story of how I benefited from one of the strategies listed above: meeting people from groups I would not usually encounter.

It is the fall of 2005, and I have just started my job as an assistant professor. I am certainly not an extrovert, but I decide to attend a party anyway, where I meet a colleague from a different department who, like me, has just been hired. We strike up a conversation and become friends. While this friendship comes to have many benefits outside of my career, it will also turn out that over the following decade, some of my most successful research efforts result from my discussions and collaborations with this friend.

In this way, allowing myself a random meeting with someone has proved a net benefit to my life. My guess is that had I allowed myself to challenge my regular routine more often and meet people I would not normally encounter, I would have a larger group of friends and acquaintances, and my interactions with those people would have enhanced my life even more.

Meeting and getting to know new people is an example of a low-harm action that, over the long term, could provide substantial benefits and significantly enrich our lives.

ENTREPRENEURSHIP AND THE POWER OF REPEATED TRIALS

Let me tell you another story about randomness, this one from a few years ago.

I take a nice vacation to a coastal area with a group of about 20 or so people, most of whom think about nothing besides which activities will give us the greatest enjoyment. I notice, however, that one person behaves differently from the rest of the group. He is often on the phone talking about work, and anywhere we go, be it a restaurant or a cruise service, he is evaluating the establishment and considering whether that type of business seems like a viable option for him. He even talks to the manager of the hotel we are staying in about whether he should build or buy a hotel in the area.

Now, I have known my business-minded friend for a long time, and I have seen him take many risks when starting businesses. He perfectly embodies the risk-taking behavior discussed in the previous section. Of course, at the beginning, he started with much smaller investments or risks. As his wealth grew, so did his investments, but he always made sure to risk only what he could afford to lose.

In my opinion, the main reason for his financial success is not just his risk-taking. It is also his attitude and his obsession with business. This is another important point that I do not think many of us appreciate enough. Now, I am not providing a value judgment here. Many of us, including me, prefer to simply enjoy our vacations without worrying about work, investments, or anything else. The thing is, when I see how much effort my friend puts into his business activities, I conclude that it is fair that he is worth tens or hundreds of times more than me. Financial success, while important, has never been my top priority. That is totally fine; we all have different priorities.

This story brings us to another interesting and useful point about randomness, luck, grit, and the power of repeated trials.

HOW MUCH DO LUCK AND SKILL INFLUENCE OUR SUCCESS?

Let's first consider the famous luck-versus-skill question. How much of our success can be attributed to luck, and how much to our hard work and skills? Here is one related personal observation. Throughout my career, I have worked with many students, researchers, and colleagues, and I have noticed that people with hardworking attitudes and plenty of motivation consistently achieve much higher levels of success than those without. So much so that within the first few months of working with doctoral students, I can often predict their level of success years into the future with a high level of accuracy.

Clearly, my small-scale anecdotal experience in a very narrow domain does not prove anything. I am not saying that luck does not matter; of course it does. When it comes to high-impact events, luck could be a huge factor. For example, a hardworking person might easily have a stroke of bad luck—say, by falling ill—that could interrupt their success. Also, when it comes to winner-take-all professions such as music, acting, and book publishing, luck could play a huge role in one's success. Regardless, the point here is that many of us underestimate the level of effort by those who achieve great success.

For example, entrepreneurship is highly risky by definition. You might hear statistics such as "85% of start-ups in a certain industry fail." However, a dedicated entrepreneur who obsessively founds start-ups and is able to start a new one right after the last one fails has a much higher chance of achieving success in the long run for two main reasons.

First, any failure comes with a lot of experience, and that experience increases the chances of future success.

Second, and more importantly, is simple probability. Even if we overlook the additional experience a serial entrepreneur brings to subsequent start-ups and assume that start-ups' outcomes are independent, the probability of achieving success in at least one start-up grows with the increasing number of attempts. We can estimate that an entrepreneur who starts eight businesses has a 73% chance of achieving success with at least one of those businesses. But, of course, this is actually a rather pessimistic calculation; the actual probability of success would likely be higher for subsequent start-ups because each one is affected by accumulated experience, knowledge, skills, connections, and so on.

Figure 4.1. The power of repeated attempts. As the number of attempts increases, success rates also increase.

Certainly, not all of us have the opportunity or willingness to be serial entrepreneurs. My point here, as shown in figure 4.1, is that by being persistent—by trying again and again—we increase our chances of achieving our goals. Also, persistent entrepreneurs can usually adapt, adjust, and pivot, all of which can effectively have the same probability impact as if we were to increase the number of trials (i.e., starting a new business).

PERSISTENCE PAYS OFF (WITH HIGH PROBABILITY)!

This discussion gives us foundational ideas behind the concepts of the power of persistence and repeated trials. As the number of attempts goes up, the probability of eventual success gets larger and larger, even if the success probability for each individual attempt is small.

This also provides a strong rationale for the well-known advice of "do what you love." If you love what you do, you continue to try, and your perseverance and repeated attempts significantly improve your probability of success. My business-minded friend may not enjoy his vacations in quite the same way as the rest of our friends, but he certainly enjoys his business undertakings; I see the delight in his eyes when he discusses his planned ventures, which is why he never stops working on his business projects, even in the middle of a vacation. When we persist in the things we love, our success increases along with our level of happiness and enjoyment.

Passion and perseverance are very powerful, as discussed in seminal books such as *Grit* (Angela Duckworth) and *Outliers* (Malcolm Gladwell). But it is important to note that this power should not be used blindly. As Annie Duke says in her fascinating book *Quit*, "Success does not lie in sticking to things. It lies in picking the right thing to stick to and quitting the rest." As always, there is a balance to be struck. Duke's book provides useful tips for identifying scenarios where we might be sticking to the wrong things. For example, it is a good idea to make sure we are not influenced by the sunk cost fallacy, endowment effect, and status quo bias.

Our probability calculation also provides some insight into when persisting is effective. Specifically, remember that probability increases when there is a certain level of statistical independence between trials. For example, when someone is attempting to innovate, utilize different approaches, or improve in some other way, their success probability amplifies. Sadly, we sometimes continue to repeat exactly what we have been doing in the past with no success without realizing such persistence is rarely beneficial.

Finally, another aspect of success through perseverance is attentiveness to opportunities. My business-minded friend is always on the lookout for business opportunities. Lucky opportunities can happen to any of us at any time, but most of the time, we are simply not paying attention. We might therefore attribute someone's success to luck when, in reality, a main reason for their success is their ability to recognize relevant opportunities when they arise. If we are not paying attention or specifically looking for something, that thing is easy to miss. This concept is beautifully illustrated in *The Invisible Gorilla* by Christopher Chabris and Daniel Simons.

In sum, our attentiveness to the opportunities around us could be another key factor in our success. We have limited attention capacity, and lots of things are constantly happening in our lives, so if we have an important goal, we should be continuously on the lookout for opportunities related to that goal.

HIGH-IMPACT DECISIONS AND EVENTS

It is January 2013, and I'm in an ambulance, scared and disoriented. We are taking my two-week-old daughter to the hospital. A mere half hour earlier, we were having fun with our newborn twin daughters, and now it seems my entire life is ending. We end up spending a few days in the hospital, and luckily she is OK.

This is an example of a potentially high-impact (harmful) event that, fortunately, ended well. In the rest of this chapter, we'll discuss events or decisions that could single-handedly change our lives. See figure 4.2.

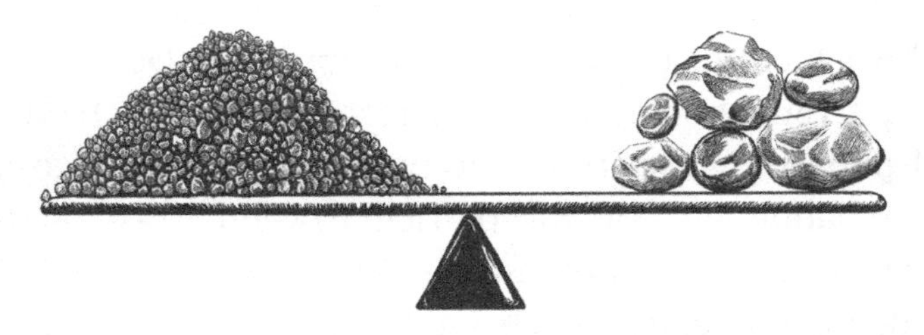

Figure 4.2. Accumulation of events. Small events (decisions) and big events both matter, and we should be careful not to underestimate either category. Small events are mostly governed by LLN (chapter 2). Big events are not.

On the surface, it might seem that the related problem statement is clear: we would like to reduce our exposure to high-impact harm and increase our exposure to high-impact gains and benefits. The discussion in the previous section on randomization and risk-taking (when the harm is limited) offered some ways to increase our exposure to high-impact positive events. Now, how do we decrease our exposure to high-impact negative events?

UNDERESTIMATED RISKS

Remember, it is easy to underestimate the accumulating impact of small decisions. When it comes to high-impact events, there is another force that could hurt us: it is also easy to underestimate the possibility and potential severity of high-stakes events. We may be aware of their importance, but we may believe they are less likely or less severe than they really are. This is partly because these events are rare; because they don't happen often, we somehow forget that they could indeed happen.

Let me provide an example of this point. For several weeks after the COVID-19 outbreak in December 2019, I remember that I underestimated the chance and potential severity of the outbreak turning into a global pandemic. This was particularly embarrassing to me as I had been aware of the potential risk of a global pandemic for years. I had even discussed it on occasion in my classes. But somehow, in my private thoughts, such a big event seemed more improbable to me than it really was. I am guessing this was partly because I had never experienced a global pandemic in my life.

In *The Black Swan*, Nassim Taleb discusses the "turkey problem." Consider a turkey that is being fed every day by a butcher. The turkey believes the butcher to be a nice person who will not harm him because it associates him with food and care. After so many hundreds of days, once the turkey has reached its adult size, the butcher kills the turkey. For the turkey, the event of this killing was statistically rare—it only happened on one day out of hundreds—so the turkey was completely oblivious to its possibility. It is easy for us to become like the turkey: we may disregard the possibility of an event simply because it is technically rare, but that same event might be inevitable.

One reason behind this so-called turkey problem is our tendency to underestimate the accumulation of risk. Next, we'll dig deeper into this issue.

RISK ACCUMULATION AND RARE EVENTS

Some time ago, I read the following two stories in the news. The first story: A bank robber successfully robs a bank.

The next day, he is easily and rapidly arrested by the police. Why? Because he returned to rob the same bank!

The second story: A burglar is woken up by the police. Apparently, he had spent the last few hours robbing various houses that night, so he got tired and decided to take a nap in the last house he was robbing!

It is easy for us to think of these people as dumb criminals and think of ourselves as having superior intelligence. However, it might be beneficial to take a deeper look at both the psychological and probabilistic phenomena behind such mistakes.

Let's assume the house robber was skilled in burglarizing homes without being detected. He may have been doing so for years and had accurately assessed that it is very unlikely that he would be caught while robbing that last house. Being caught in a single robbery is a low-probability event; however, as he continues to repeatedly burglarize, his probability of being caught goes up for two reasons.

First, like the serial entrepreneur discussed earlier, there is probability amplification in repeated experiments. In other words, over time, the *accumulated risk* increases. Second, the house robber gets more confident with each successful burglary. He perceives being caught as a less and less likely event to the point where he begins to think it is impossible for him to be caught. He becomes a complete turkey. His complacency causes him to become so sloppy that he decides to take a nap during the last robbery.

Just to be clear here, I am not implying that it is OK to rob "only" a few houses. You should rob exactly zero houses. And incidentally, if you do rob a house, under no circumstances should you choose to nap there.

The key point is that we must acknowledge *accumulated risk*. As another example, I know that using hard drugs is dangerous. But say I try them anyway someday, maybe due to peer pressure. Nothing bad happens. The next time I'm offered them, my belief that a tragic accident could occur is lower, since a tragic accident did not occur the last time. After a while, my drug use at parties becomes more frequent. Then, at some point, I overdose. The probability of an overdose due to a single isolated drug use may be low, but when that use becomes a repeated habit, my accumulated risk of becoming very ill or overdosing gets higher and higher.

In sum, it is a big mistake to consider only the risk involved in an isolated action. Repeated exposure amplifies risk.

THE HIDDEN (OR IGNORED) ACCUMULATED RISK

Suppose you live in a rural area with little traffic. Your neighbor tells you he plans to close his eyes, take a walk, and start shooting a gun in random directions. You become outraged! You tell him this idea is dangerous; he might kill or seriously injure someone. He tells you: "Oh, my friend, you are uneducated. I recently read a probability textbook by Hossein Pishro-Nik, and I have calculated the exact probability that I might hit someone. In this uncrowded area, the probability that I will hit someone in my 30-minute walk is less than one percent."

I am guessing you don't buy his argument. First of all, how can he exactly compute the probability? The word *exact* here is a bit misleading due to the nature of the problem. Second, even if the probability really is less than 1%, since the harm could be catastrophic (killing or seriously injuring someone), the risk is not one you are willing to allow him to take. And incidentally, who is this Pishro-Nik guy, anyway?

Finally, with this attitude, your neighbor is demonstrating an underestimation of accumulated risk. It may be the case that no one is hurt on his first walk, but if he repeats such actions—which he seems likely to do with this kind of attitude—he will eventually instigate a disaster.

I'm with you on this opinion. But this imaginary story does not end there, so let's look at the rest of it. It is the middle of a nasty pandemic with a lot of unknowns. You are instructed to follow strict safety measures such as avoiding gatherings or unnecessary travel. You follow the advice for a week or so and then get tired of it. You tell yourself, "I am young and healthy," so you start attending gatherings and slacking off on other safety measures.

Soon, you bump into your gun-firing neighbor, and he asks you what you have been up to lately. You confess that you have not been very careful with pandemic measures. Now your neighbor is outraged. He asks, "Don't you know you have been endangering people? How do you know you are not carrying the virus and infecting older or otherwise vulnerable people? Many people are asymptomatic, you know."

You respond, "But that is very unlikely." Your neighbor asks, "How unlikely? How is it different from the likelihood of me injuring someone by shooting randomly in an uncrowded area?"

Allow me not to take part in this fictional debate. The reality is that there are a host of complicated issues here beyond just risk management. Nevertheless, we can point out one issue relevant to our discussion on risk: some forms of risks are vivid and obvious, and others are less so. For example, almost everyone agrees that randomly shooting a gun in a residential area, no matter how uncrowded, is not acceptable. However, in many instances, accumulated risk is not obvious, which makes it very easy to underestimate. Again, this tells us that carefully considering potential harm could help us make better decisions.

INSURANCE, FLEXIBILITY, AND MARGINS

Paying attention to the accumulation of risk is one way to potentially reduce our exposure to high-impact harm, but another strategy that could help in this regard is called *flexible planning*. The simplest form of this strategy is insurance.

We sometimes fall prey to the low probability of events and do not buy enough insurance. An Uber driver once told me that he was saving a lot of money each month by not paying for health insurance. His reasoning was that "I am healthy, so I don't even need it." Those of us with health insurance might believe we have better judgment than that, but many of us fall into similar traps when it comes to other types of insurance.

For many potentially harmful events, there are types of insurance available that can help soften the blow should the event arise. One important action item, then, is to research different types of insurance and make sure we are sufficiently insured for our particular lifestyles. Everyone's situation is different, but many of us can benefit from sufficient health insurance, auto insurance, home insurance, disability insurance, life insurance, and long-term care insurance, to name a few. We never know when something might happen that requires us to use these policies, but someday *something* will happen.

Due to our fundamental uncertainty, we cannot predict the future, so it makes sense to plan in a way that gives us the most flexibility. Any form of margin that we discussed previously can be thought of as a way to increase our flexibility in the face of uncertainty.

Again, an important point here is that we could easily forget about the need for such flexibility. For example, when the stock and housing markets are doing well, the net worth of investors becomes larger. Evidence shows that in these circumstances, some people retire earlier than planned due to this perceived increase in wealth. However, this could be a risky move since markets are unpredictable and can go down again at any time. In this case, it may be a wise idea to make sure we have enough margins to sustain ourselves during market downfalls. Even though it is not explicitly called *insurance*, this margin acts as a sort of insurance against obstacles to our success such as a market downturn.

THE ULTIMATE DEFENSE AGAINST NEGATIVE EVENTS

We have discussed some tools for reducing our exposure to high-impact negative events, but what else does our understanding of fundamental uncertainty tell us about such events? It simply tells us that we cannot fully eliminate their possibility.

Whether we like it or not, at some point in our lives, we may well face horrible events. Disease, an unfortunate accident, a loss of life, or a crushing Super Bowl loss to the rival team are all very real possibilities. One strong defense against these potential events, then, would be to learn how to minimize our suffering when they inevitably happen.

The good news is that this self-protection is quite possible. Methods by which one can achieve this self-protection will differ from person to person, of course, ranging from religion, spirituality, stoicism, or some other philosophy, and so on. Whatever the case, many people have achieved the strength to deal with stark adversity. I have personally witnessed people who stood strong against immense hardships such as the loss of a child or a terminal diagnosis.

The uncertainty mindset tells us all to develop a plan and aim to fortify ourselves against such adversities. I have not fully achieved this for myself (I have not yet recovered from Brazil's 7–1 loss in the 2014 World Cup); nevertheless, I think I have made significant progress. Just being aware of the need to fortify yourself against unexpected negative everts will help you make progress too.

CHAPTER TAKEAWAYS

- Potential harm is a good metric that can help in categorizing decisions and actions. Actions with significant potential harm are put in the potentially "harmful" category, and those with a limited potential harm are put in the "safe" category.
- Satisficing can be an effective method for making low-impact decisions. This strategy saves time and energy and often reduces regret.
- We tend to underestimate the power of randomness, and we are often too afraid of small losses. When harm is limited, it pays to take more risks as the rewards of such risk-taking could be significant in the long term.
- It is a good idea to purposefully allocate a portion of our time to exploring and trying new things when the potential harm is limited. Examples include trying random unfamiliar activities, interacting with new groups, and playing with unorthodox ideas at work.
- Repeated attempts magnify the probability of success; this provides a foundation for the power of persistence. This is a strong argument for doing what we love; in the long run, it is much easier to persist in something you enjoy.
- Paying attention to new opportunities could be another key factor in our success. If we have important goals, we should be continuously on the lookout for opportunities related to those goals.

- For potentially harmful events, it is important to consider the accumulation of risk. We often underestimate accumulated risk since in the short term, this risk is not visible.
- It is a big mistake to look only at the risk of an action in isolation. Repeated exposure amplifies that risk.
- Be aware of accumulated risks that are not direct, obvious, or explicit. We all understand the dangers of guns, but there are other things we might not perceive as risky as guns that could in fact be much more dangerous.
- Incorporating insurance, margins, and flexibility in our lives is another approach to reducing our exposure to high-impact negative events.
- Fundamental uncertainty tells us we cannot eliminate all risks. A useful life philosophy would be one that minimizes our suffering when faced with a highly unfortunate and unforeseen event. Observation tells us this is achievable.

CHAPTER 5:
NONLINEARITY AND ITS SURPRISING IMPACT

Let's start this chapter with a riddle. Bob is an investor who starts out with $1 million. Over a 20-year period, his investment returns an average gain of 10% annually. By the end of the period, he has lost about 80% of his money. How could this be?

You may have figured out that the answer to this riddle lies in the word *average*. Say that to achieve this 10% average gain, Bob has a gain of 55% half of the time and a loss of 45% the other half. It is true that the *arithmetic* average of returns is a positive 10%, but the arithmetic average is mostly irrelevant here. If you were to gain 55% in the first year and lose 45% in the second year, you would already have an overall net loss of 14.75%. This is what happened to Bob.

This is a simple example of *nonlinearity*. In fact, there are many subtler and more consequential ways that nonlinearity impacts our lives (even for those of us who are not investors).

In chapter 2, we discussed the law of large numbers (LLN). Specifically, we mentioned that there are three required conditions for LLN to hold: (1) independence, (2) low impact, and (3) linearity. If any of these assumptions are not valid, then we would find ourselves in uncharted territory and could not rely on LLN being true. In the last chapter, we touched on one assumption—the low-impact assumption—in relation to high-impact events. In this chapter and the next, we will discuss nonlinearity and dependence, both of which can have a surprisingly enormous impact on our affairs.

It turns out that in many situations in life and business, both nonlinearity and dependence are present and related to each other. Armed with the concepts in these chapters, we can take advantage of them and avoid being harmed by them.

WHAT IS NONLINEARITY?

It is the fall of 1998. I'm in college, eating a huge lunch and, like an idiot, ignoring the fact that I have to take a physical education (PE) exam at 2:00 p.m. I go to PE class with a full stomach. The exam, known as the Cooper test, is a test of physical fitness consisting of a possible 24 points. To get the full 24 points, we are supposed to finish running 24 laps around the university pool in 12 minutes.

I start strong and am confident that I will do well. Midway through the test, however, I feel a sharp pain in my stomach. Soon, I start to feel *horrible*. I am forced to choose between my health and my pride. Being a good decision-maker, I choose my pride. In my mind, I feel like a brave soldier sacrificing his life for his country. (I know; it's a ridiculous analogy. I've already said I was an idiot.) I manage to finish exactly 22 laps before collapsing on the ground, consoling myself that even if I didn't finish, at least I have done well under the circumstances: since 24 laps means full credit, I should get 22 points for 22 laps, right?

That's when the PE instructor approaches me and, completely disregarding my horrible condition, writes a big fat zero on his clipboard in front of my name. What happened to my points? It turns out the grading for the Cooper test is nonlinear. In other words, not all laps have the same number of points. The first 22 laps are worth 0 points per lap, and from the 22nd lap to the 24th lap, your grade gradually increases from 0 to 24. This was the first time I realized that nonlinearity could hurt me. (Luckily, I performed better in other PE exams and managed to pass PE class.)

When the impacts of multiple things are added to each other straightforwardly to create a whole, we have a linear situation. In the PE example, the grading system would have been linear if I had gotten 1 point for each lap. Unfortunately for me, it was not—but many aspects of life are indeed linear. For example, an employee who gets paid $30 an hour is being paid linearly; the amount they earn is directly proportional to the number of hours they work.

On the other hand, many aspects of our personal, business, and social lives are nonlinear. The pleasure you receive from having two ice cream cones on a hot day is not twice the pleasure of one ice cream cone. A third ice cream cone might even result in displeasure.[8] When combined with uncertainty and randomness, nonlinearities could have huge consequences. Let's try to better understand how we can take advantage of nonlinearities and, at the same time, avoid being harmed by nonlinear effects.

Before we begin, however, let me address an issue you may have noticed. The problem is that there are so many different types of nonlinearities. (The scientist Stanislaw Ulam was once reported to have said, "Using a term like *nonlinear science* is like referring to the bulk of zoology as the study of non-elephant animals.") In this chapter, we will limit our discussion to a few important types of nonlinearities.

Let's go back to elementary school, where we all (hopefully) learned addition, which, as I mentioned, creates linearity. We also learned multiplication in elementary school. Multiplication, on the other hand, can create nonlinearity, which could have important implications for risk management and decision-making.

RANDOM MULTIPLICATIVE PROCESSES (MP)

Here is another riddle. An intelligent investor named Mr. IQ started with $1 and, after 20 years, turned his $1 investment into $1 million. Assuming his rate of return was the same each year, how much was his investment worth after 15 years? A bit of math shows that the investor had less than $32,000 at the end of year 15. This means that in the first 15 years, Mr. IQ made only 3% of his overall gain; he made 97% of his gain in the last 5 years. This is shown in figure 5.1.

8 Economists refer to such nonlinearities as the *law of diminishing marginal utility*.

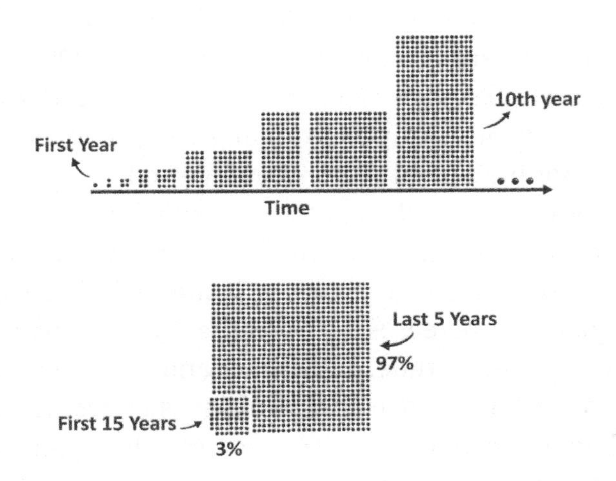

Figure 5.1. The power of compounding (exponential growth). This example is a special case of a multiplicative process, where no randomness or uncertainty is involved. However, in most real-life multiplicative processes, uncertainty is present, which further complicates planning.

Most of us are familiar with the power of compounding: the income from an asset is reinvested, thus making yet more income. Compounding is a special case of multiplicative processes (MP). MPs are an important class of nonlinearities; they often exhibit counterintuitive effects and can have surprising impacts on our lives, specifically when uncertainty and randomness are present.

Let's get more specific about what we mean in this book by a multiplicative process. Here, the term *multiplicative process* describes what happens when the outcome is obtained by multiplying the individual factors. For example, in investments, your money is multiplied each year by a growth or loss factor for that year. If you have a 10% loss in a certain year, your total investment is multiplied by a factor of 90% or 0.9. Therefore, the value of your investment after several years is calculated by multiplying the growth or loss factors for individual years in that period.

One way to think about a multiplicative process is to consider a scenario in which a quantity changes by some percentage of its current value. In other words, the quantity increases or decreases in proportion to its current magnitude. In finance and investment, we usually look at the percentage of the changes; we say a stock index increased by 10% last year. In a pandemic, we also look at the growth percentage; every infected person could result in multiple additional infections. In both cases, there is a multiplying factor that could result in exponential growth (or decline).

The fact that there is usually randomness—i.e., the growth or loss factor for each period cannot be predicted beforehand with certainty—makes such multiplicative processes interesting and sometimes dangerous to work with.

OK. Now that we know what MPs are, how can we take advantage of them and avoid being harmed by them?

THE DAMAGING EFFECT OF LOSSES: RISK MANAGEMENT

Let's return to finance. You may have heard about Warren Buffett's rules for investing: "Rule number one is never lose money. Rule number two is never forget rule number one." Since these rules come from a smart guy like Buffett, we might suspect there is something deeper than the obvious at work in the above statement—and there is. A good way to think about the importance of losses is to note how investment returns work as a multiplicative process.

Remember the example at the beginning of this chapter: if you lose 45% of your money and then earn a 55% gain, you have effectively lost 14.75% of your money. Why? Because the gain is being made on a lesser amount. Let's look at an even simpler example: if you lose 30% and then gain 30%, you have lost 9%. Similarly, if you first gain 30% and then lose 30%, again you have lost 9%, since your 30% loss is on a bigger amount.

What can we learn from these examples? When you are investing over a period of time, your total return compounds. This means that any percentage of loss impacts you more than the equivalent percentage of gain. One way to think about this is that when you lose a percentage of your money, you also lose any compounding growth that this lost money could have been earning for you in the future. As simple as it sounds, this can have a profound effect on investments.

How can we use this idea practically? One way to appreciate this lesson is to consider the role of low-risk assets, as well as assets that might act as insurance. When investing, it may be tempting to focus only on assets with the highest potential for returns such as stocks. With this mindset, keeping money in cash or treasury bills might seem dull and wasteful. However, given the damaging impact of potential losses in a multiplicative process, including low-risk assets in your portfolio could be a wise move.

The reverse is true when it comes to borrowing. I think of borrowing as having negative cash in my portfolio. If times are good and I am gaining, borrowing could magnify my gains—but if there is a market crash, debt could wipe me out. Again, the key point is that losses are mathematically more harmful than equivalent percentage-wise gains.

That's why I personally think the most important lessons for a small investor like me are to keep a portion of my money in low-risk assets (such as checking or savings accounts, certificates of deposit, and treasury bills), and to try to avoid borrowing. This strategy might not be optimal in terms of potential returns, but it certainly provides some peace of mind. Of course, I am not a financial adviser, and I only manage my own small portfolio. Luckily, we can learn from professional investors. There is a long list of outstanding figures who investigated investments in the form of various multiplicative processes, including Daniel Bernoulli, John Larry Kelly Jr, Edward Thorp, and Benoit Mandelbrot.[9]

RONALD READ'S SECRET TO SUCCESS

In chapter 2, I mentioned the story of Ronald Read, who, at the time of his death, had acquired about $8 million despite having a relatively low-paying job. He was able to leave millions of dollars to charities in his will. As we discussed, he managed this through the power of repetitive low-impact actions—specifically, his small,

9 The excellent book *Safe Haven* by Mark Spitznagel goes deeper into the points made here and could be insightful for someone managing a portfolio's risk.

repetitive contributions to savings and investing accounts—which allowed Mr. Read to accomplish this honorable goal.

However, now that we have discussed multiplicative processes, we can gain even more insight into Mr. Read's situation. Based on the available reports, it seems that Mr. Read's investments were almost all in stocks. If true, this might have made him potentially vulnerable to the damaging effects of multiplicative losses.

Had Mr. Read's life span shifted slightly so that his passing occurred in the middle of a recession, his total wealth might have been significantly less than $8 million—possibly as low as $4 or even $3 million. This is still a large sum, of course, but it would have significantly reduced his charitable donations. Luckily for those charities, the timing worked out OK.

What do we learn from this? The last factor that helped Mr. Read leave a large charitable donation was, essentially, luck. The timing was on his side, especially since he lived for 92 years. But from the point of view of risk management, it might have been wise for Mr. Read to have a more diverse categories of assets in his portfolio, for example, by allocating a certain percentage of his money to low-risk assets such as fixed-income securities.

MAXIMIZING BENEFITS FROM EXPONENTIAL GROWTH

So far, we have learned from our discussion that in a beneficial multiplicative process, it is crucial to alleviate losses. Now, let's discuss a few other things related to multiplicative processes. We're all aware of the power of compounding and exponential growth; any time there is multiplicative growth, time is your best friend. As we see in Mr. IQ's example, the last five years of his investing accounted for 97% of his gain. In other words, if Mr. IQ had started five years later than his original start date, he would have missed the biggest part of his gain.

This fact is why, when it comes to saving and investing for retirement, it is extremely important to start early. If you are young, time is on your side, but each delay could drastically hurt your portfolio. Therefore, a good general rule would be the following: in a beneficial multiplicative growth situation, take advantage of time whenever possible.

OK, nothing unusual here. You probably knew this already. But there are two subtle points I want to emphasize.

First, although most of us know the importance of time to multiplicative growth, we often fail to act on this knowledge. To counter this, we might significantly benefit from the psychological tricks we discussed in chapter 2. For example, automating our investments could be very effective in this regard, as well as using other commitment devices that we discussed.

Second, there are other scenarios that have similar dynamics as multiplicative growth but are not exactly the same thing, and those scenarios might be easy to miss. For example, the learning curve for acquiring some skills might be similar to an exponential curve, at least in the beginning stages: for a long period of time, very little progress is observed, and then suddenly, in a very short period, progress might accelerate. Learning to play the violin, mastering swimming or ice hockey, and learning to type on a keyboard are potential examples of this phenomenon. In each of these cases, we may observe little progress for a long time. Then, with commitment and persistence, the skills come together one day at a level that might surprise us. Scientific research often follows a similar pattern of long periods of no results followed by sharp progress in a relatively short time period. In some domains, new businesses might also take such a path: significant effort involving trial and error, research, product development, and testing might be required at the beginning, where not much visible gain is observed, followed by a shorter period of significant growth.

When faced with such endeavors, many of us quit too early—we give in during the slow-progress phase because we don't see the results we've hoped for. The people who persist are the ones who actually make it to the fast-progress phase and then reap the rewards. The example we keep returning to in this chapter is wealth creation. If your goal is financial success, it is helpful to be aware that you are most likely in an exponential-like situation. For several years, it might feel that you are making very slow progress, but if you persist, you have a good chance of eventually reaching the fast-progress phase.

The media often magnifies stories of people who become billionaires in their teens or early twenties. These are extremely rare situations that have little relevance to the rest of us. Many people who achieve high levels of financial success make the most effective gains in their forties and fifties. These are usually the people who have persisted in their efforts and made it through the slow-progress phases with patience and perseverance.

AVOIDING HARMS FROM EXPONENTIAL GROWTH

A similar phenomenon, where a long period of slow growth is followed by a short period of rapid growth, is present in harmful multiplicative processes. That is why, for example, the first stages of a pandemic are so crucial; after the full power of compounding has been realized and thousands of people are infected and contagious, it will be very difficult to stop the spread among a population. This situation might also be present in the growth of cancer cells, where early detection could be important for defeating the growth inside a body.

In personal finance, debt could also act as a harmful multiplicative process. If you do not pay off your credit cards, your total debt grows by the corresponding interest rate each month. If you are not careful, you could accumulate a large amount of debt in this way. Not surprisingly, this particular exponential process is harmful to you but very beneficial and lucrative to credit card companies.

FOREST FIRE DETECTION PROJECT

Allow me to provide an example of how I have personally used the concept of exponential growth. Before I do, remember that in a harmful exponential growth scenario, early detection and intervention could be crucial. Therefore, it is important to quickly identify such scenarios.

As we all know, forest fires can be devastating. They can cover gigantic areas and result in billions of dollars in suppression efforts and property costs in addition to potential human and animal fatalities. We can think of such fires as harmful multiplicative processes: after an initial interval where the fire is still small, it can enter a period where it spreads quickly and exponentially. Detected too late, forest fires could incur heavy costs and damage vast areas. Therefore, if we can find a way to detect dangerous fires early on when they are still small, we could potentially save millions of acres of forest land as well as billions of dollars. Early detection can be crucial to our ability to control a wildfire.

Using this insight, with the help of students in my research group, I designed a system of drones that could fly regularly over a forested area and use image recognition algorithms to detect fires. Given that drones are becoming more powerful and widespread, such systems could end up being an effective and affordable way of alleviating forest fire problems.

THE WEIRD WORLD OF MPS

OK—time to have some fun with an experiment that will expose some of the subtler aspects of MPs. It's been a while since we tossed some coins, so let's do that now. We're going to gather a large group of people and hand out some money. Since we're feeling generous, to begin with, let's give each member of our group $1,000. We'll also give each of them a fair coin, which will eventually be used to determine their total earnings.

Here is how the experiment goes: Each player tosses their coin 1,000 times. For each heads, the player receives a 25% gain on their current balance. For each tails, the player takes a 20% loss. What kind of outcomes do you expect at the end of the experiment? After 1,000 tosses, the results turn out to be quite interesting.

First, let's look at the people who end up in the bottom 30% of earners. These players each have $28.00 or less. How about the bottom 10%? These players have 13 cents or less! What about the bottom 5%? These unlucky players have less than a single cent!

Next, let's look at the people in the top 30%. These lucky players now have $35,000 or more. Not bad! How about the top 10%? These players have acquired more than $7.5 million each! And the top 5%? They now have more than $100 million!

Are you surprised? In fact, the above results are not actually the most surprising part of this experiment. We'll go into the reasons for this in a moment, but first, let me ask you the following question: What is the average outcome for the players in the experiment? Go on, make a guess. (Remember, I am referring to the statistical concept of the *expected value*, which we reviewed in chapters 2 and 4.)

Ready for the answer? It turns out that the expected average wealth for a player in this game is more than $50 *trillion*! That is, the average gain from this coin toss game is hundreds of thousands of times larger than the threshold for being in the top 5%.

SOME PROPERTIES OF MPS

The goal of this coin-tossing example—other than to make you jealous that you were not invited to participate—is to expose some of the subtleties of MPs. As I mentioned earlier, the effects of MPs are present in processes such as wealth creation and can have counter-intuitive results on our affairs, so it's good to be aware of these effects. Note that in some sense, the coin-tossing example has some similarities to investing in the stock market. A large number of players (investors) invest in the market, and each month or year, each of them will get some returns on their investment. Such vivid examples help us better realize the magnitude of the situation and the risks involved in MPs.

Let's take note of a couple of points here:

- There are gigantic disparities in the wealth outcome of the players in the game; the range of possibilities is ridiculously vast.
- These disparities could occur regardless of the player's skill. They could happen due to randomness and the compounding effect of the MPs.
- Rare outcomes could be massive and therefore significantly distort the average (expected value).
- The most probable values could be significantly different from the expected value, usually due to the impact of rare events.

So what lessons can we learn? The first lesson is that it is shockingly easy to get crushed by an MP. In our coin toss experiment, there is a 30% chance that a player will end up with less than $28, even though they started with $1,000. Thus, my first real-world action item is to plan for significant negative consequences when investing, perhaps by increasing the proportion of low-risk assets even though they come with a lower expected return.

Second, we must be skeptical when people cite averages or expected values. Due to the disproportionate impact of rare outcomes, the true average is difficult to estimate in the first place—but more importantly, the average could largely be irrelevant anyway. Here, for example, almost all players earn significantly below average. Therefore, we must be wary of trusting averages in such situations.

The final lesson relates to the importance of *heavy-tailed* distributions, which we will discuss next.[10] Before you read the next section, let me provide a clarification: the word *tailed* in the expression *heavy-tailed* does not have anything to do with heads or "tails" in the coin-tossing example.

HEAVY-TAILED VERSUS LIGHT-TAILED DISTRIBUTIONS

It is 7:00 in the evening. More than 100 students are sitting in a large lecture hall taking a two-hour exam for my course. I feel a bit guilty about this; for the next two hours, I will be sitting at the front of the room pretending to work, while these poor students have to go through a long exam. I try to alleviate my guilt and

10 Related discussions on this topic usually appear under different terms such as *fat-tailed distributions*, *power laws*, and *scale invariance*. The term *heavy-tailed distributions* used here is usually assumed to be a general term including others. Good discussions on these topics can be found in *The Misbehavior of Markets* by Benoit B. Mandelbrot and *The Black Swan* by Nassim Taleb.

comfort the students with the following announcement:

"I know you all probably don't think it's fair that you have to take an exam for the next two hours while I am just sitting here relaxing. However, if you think about it, you are in a much better position than me. You see, you are much younger, which means that in all likelihood, you will outlive me. Therefore, you will be able to take your revenge: think about the fact that when I die, you will still have decades left to live."

OK, maybe my statement is overly dramatic, but I have a valid statistical point. The mere fact that I am much older than most of my students means that I most likely have much less time left. The reason for this is that a human lifetime follows what we call a *light-tailed distribution*.

Now, what do I mean by that? Roughly speaking, in a light-tailed environment, extreme observations are almost impossible. A person will not live for 2,000 years; there is no one taller than 10 feet. Human life span and height are examples of light-tailed variables. Stated simply, in a light-tailed environment, extreme deviations from normal values are almost impossible.

The opposite of this would be a *heavy-tailed distribution* such as wealth distrubution, where we might witness enormous deviations from the norm. A single rich person might have more wealth than a million other people combined. In heavy-tailed environments like this, the impact of extreme values could be huge. We saw an example of this in our coin-tossing experiment: extra care is needed when dealing with heavy tails.

For now, you can remember this: in heavy-tailed environments, there can be a wide range of possible values, and wild deviations from what we may think of as normal or typical values are possible. In fact, due to such wild variations, there is usually no typical or normal value. The following table provides a summary of some of the key differences between heavy-tailed and light-tailed distributions.

Heavy-Tailed Properties and Examples	**Light-Tailed Properties and Examples**
Potentially huge deviation from projected norms or average	Little deviation from projected norms or average
Career examples include entrepreneurs or novelists	Career examples include teachers or nurses
Epidemics of infectious diseases	Death from home accidents
Wealth distribution	Human lifespan
Preparations include limiting negative risks	Less fear of downsides

One example of a heavy-tailed environment is the example of epidemics discussed earlier: because of the possibility of an enormous outcome, millions or billions of people could be impacted. The range of possibilities is vast. On the other hand, many other dangers are fairly stable. For example, the number of people dying from slip-and-fall accidents does not show gigantic variations from year to year, and we do not normally worry about millions or billions of people suddenly dying this way.

NONLINEARITY CAN CAUSE HEAVY-TAILED DISTRIBUTIONS

Let's recap. In this chapter, we are discussing the impact of nonlinearity. We mentioned that one reason nonlinearity is important is that it can result in heavy-tailed distributions. We saw this in the earlier coin-tossing example, which is a simplified version of wealth outcome from investment. This was a multiplicative process, an example of a nonlinear process. We observed gigantic variations in wealth outcomes, which is consistent with a heavy-tailed environment.

What's the main takeaway here? In general, it is important to identify whether you are in a heavy-tailed or light-tailed environment. In a light-tailed scenario, extreme deviations from the norm are almost impossible. You do not hear of a teacher earning a $10 million salary. However, there are business owners who earn much more than that. The reverse is also true; more business owners go fully broke than teachers. As we saw in the previous table, being a teacher is an example of a light-tailed scenario, while being a business owner is a heavy-tailed environment.

STRATEGIES FOR HEAVY-TAILED ENVIRONMENTS

Given the enormous differences between heavy-tailed and light-tailed environments, dealing with each requires a different mindset. One important thing to remember is that in a heavy-tailed environment, it is crucial to limit the downside risk. We discussed this issue as it relates to financial portfolios, but a similar situation exists in other scenarios.

As we learned, professions such as writers, actors, and entrepreneurs fall into the heavy-tailed category in the sense that the majority of people who enter these professions do not earn much money, while a very tiny portion goes on to achieve extraordinary success. So, what would be a reasonable approach for someone who aspires to become a successful writer, actor, or entrepreneur?

As I mentioned, limiting negative risk is important in such environments. This connects back to our previous discussion on leaving room for margins. For example, suppose you want to be a novelist. You know that if you model your career only on those of extremely successful authors, your view of your chances of similar success will be distorted. There are many, many more unknown and less-successful authors in the world. Recognizing that you are in a heavy-tailed situation, you decide you want to limit your risks.

If you decide to pursue a career as a novelist, you might decide to start small. Perhaps you get a degree from a good college in a related field, try to get jobs in publishing or related industries, and build experience and connections. By doing so, you will increase your margin and reduce your risks by being able to financially support yourself with a steady career, and you will make contacts that could help further your writing career. This way, if you are ultimately unsuccessful as an author due to the low odds, you have a degree, your career, and your savings to protect you.

As a final example, if you decide to start a business, you can limit your risk through something called *hybrid entrepreneurship*, where you might start your business while keeping your current employment. If your start-up does not take off, you still have a career and a steady income. On the other hand, if your start-up eventually grows, and you observe a promising path to success, you always have the option of quitting your day job to focus on your business.

CHAPTER TAKEAWAYS

- It is important to distinguish between linear and nonlinear environments. In a linear environment, you can simply add the impact of each individual component to obtain the total impact. For example, an hourly worker's earnings are proportional to the number of hours they work. In a nonlinear environment, this is not the case, so the outcomes are more difficult to predict.
- There are many different types of nonlinearities. Random multiplicative processes (MP) are one important class of nonlinear processes.
- MPs are those in which the total effect is obtained by multiplying the individual factors. Financial outcomes over years of investing or saving and the growth of pandemics are both examples of MPs.
- An important and often overlooked lesson regarding MPs is that any percentage of loss impacts you more than the equivalent percentage of gain. In an MP environment, avoiding major losses should be a primary goal.
- Random MPs usually create a large range of possible values. It is easy to end up at the bottom of a group simply due to bad luck, but we can try to protect ourselves by applying tools that limit the negative risks. In finance, this might be done

by diversifying investments into safer assets and limiting debt.

- In an MP, averages or expected values are often irrelevant. Thus, any stated average value could be misleading. Anytime we hear "on average," we should ask ourselves if we are in a light-tailed or heavy-tailed environment. If the latter, then we should put less value on the stated average.
- A simple rule regarding the exponential growth environment is the following: In a beneficial exponential growth situation such as retirement investing, education, skill learning, or business building, maximizing time should be an important goal. In a harmful exponential growth situation such as debt, a pandemic, some diseases, or a forest fire, early detection and prevention could be crucial.
- Acquiring a new skill, learning an unfamiliar topic, and starting a business venture usually follow nonlinear paths. In some scenarios, the path might resemble an exponential curve: you obtain very little in the beginning stages, but if you persist, you might enter a fast-progress phase. The awareness that we are in such a scenario could help us sustain our efforts during the slow-progress phase.
- It is important to know if you are dealing with a heavy-tailed or light-tailed scenario. In a light-tailed scenario, extreme deviations from the norm are almost impossible. Being a teacher is

an example of a light-tailed scenario, while being a business owner can be a heavy-tailed scenario.

- In some scenarios, we can limit negative risk by mixing a heavy-tailed scenario with a light-tailed scenario. An aspiring entrepreneur can start small by earning a related degree, securing a job in a related field to gain experience and understand the field better, and growing their business gradually while sustaining a regular income.

CHAPTER 6:
THE POWER OF DEPENDENCY AND BAYESIAN THINKING

It is a cold winter's night, and I am upstairs, alone in the house. Suddenly, I hear a sound that seems to come from my laundry room downstairs. It sounds like someone has broken in. However, I smile and give myself a pat on the back; many years of experience in probability and statistics have given me a good understanding of what's probably going on. I am not worried, because I know that the odds that some intruder is in the house are extremely small. The most likely scenario is that something fell and created the noise I heard.

Nevertheless, I am curious to see what happened, so I go downstairs to check the laundry room—but when I reach for the door handle and try to push open the door, I feel resistance. It seems there is a person behind the door, pushing back, not letting me open it. In a split second, my totally calm and relaxed state of mind is transformed into one of alarm and panic. I push hard to open the door, but the more I push, the harder the intruder pushes back.

I make one last attempt, pushing with all my power, and eventually burst through the door. What I see is not pretty. It takes me about 10 seconds to figure out what has happened. Finally, feeling very embarrassed, I start to laugh.

Here is what happened. There was a mop hanging upside down on the wall behind the laundry room door. The mop had fallen, creating the noise I'd heard. Incidentally, the mop had landed in an interesting position: the head of the mop was leaning against the door handle from the inside of the laundry room, and the end of the mop was propped against the wall. This meant the mop was acting as a brace against the door. The mop handle was made of plastic or some other flexible material, so the more I pushed, the more the mop bent. To me, it felt like someone was resisting my attempts to open the door.

This story raises two interesting points. The first is that what we may think of as the old, instinctual brain can easily override the new, supposedly logical brain. Anything related to survival, such as perceived danger, usually causes the old brain to kick in, which is why as soon as I felt the pushback on the door, all my probabilistic training and logical thinking vanished, and the old brain took control.

The second point is related to a concept known as Bayesian thinking (named after the statistician and philosopher Thomas Bayes) in which we measure and update our assumptions and beliefs based on our observations of the world. This concept will be discussed later in the chapter among other aspects of dependency as they relate to decision-making. First, let's begin by briefly discussing dependency and its importance.

DEPENDENCE IS THE KEY: VIRAL VIDEOS, PANDEMICS, AND WEALTH DISPARITY

So far in this book, we have overlooked one important aspect of decision-making: that events and decisions impact other events and decisions. Our decisions impact our later decisions and influence other people, and other people's decisions also impact us and our decisions. If you think about it, we are in a massive web of events, decisions, and people in which every node in the network impacts many other nodes. In sum, events and decisions depend on other events and decisions. In this section, we will explore this issue and learn how we can benefit from it.

One important aspect of this dependence relates to Bayesian thinking, which essentially helps us update our view regarding uncertain situations in the face of evidence or observations. This could potentially help us improve our decision-making in any given situation.

VIRAL VIDEOS AND PANDEMICS

In chapter 5, we saw how dependence is a major driver of nonlinearity. Consider the example of viral phenomena, which includes actual viruses, viral videos, viral songs, and so much more. Why are epidemics so dangerous and viral videos so popular? It's because they are examples of a multiplicative process: each infected person could infect others. Therefore, the number of infected people can grow in proportion to the number of currently infected people. As we discussed, this can generate exponential growth, which in turn could create a heavy-tailed environment.

Now, the key point here is dependence. Every person who gets infected increases the probability of others being infected. If a person near you is infected, the probability of you also becoming infected increases. In other words, this statistical dependence is what creates the multiplicative phenomenon and exponential growth.

THE RICH GET RICHER

Similar dynamics are often present in career or business success. Your first success might give you an edge in the following stages of your career, again potentially creating a multiplicative process. This is one of the key reasons behind the *rich-get-richer phenomenon* and could partly explain the reason for wild deviations in business success or wealth size. As you recall, business success is usually a heavy-tailed environment.

Let's do another quick coin toss experiment to get some insights. We are going to divide $1,000 between two players, A and B. We'll do the experiment in two different ways: a boring way and a fun way.

First, let's play the boring way. We toss a coin 1,000 times. With each heads, we give a dollar to player A, and with each tails, we give a dollar to player B. After 1,000 coin tosses, the money has been divided between A and B. We can expect each player to receive about the same amount, but due to randomness, one lucky player might end up with a bit more money than the other. With this method, on average, the lucky player will only have about 5% more money than the unlucky player. Here, we are in a light-tailed environment, and the law of large numbers (LLN) is at work.

Now, let's play the fun way. We give each player a dollar to begin with. Next, we toss a coin—but this is a special, biased coin that favors whichever player has more money at the time of the toss. This means that a player who won a bit more money in previous stages of the game is more likely to win the current coin toss. Let's say that using this special coin, the probability of one player winning the next dollar is proportional to that player's current wealth. For example, the first coin toss of the game gives each player a 50/50 chance of success. But suppose at one stage of the game, player A has $22 and player B has $18. Because player A has 55% of the current wealth, that player has a 55% probability of winning the next round.

What do you think might happen by the end of the game when the $1,000 has been divided between A and B? On average, the lucky player will have more than *12 times* the amount of the other player! This experiment can help us better understand how dependency can propel the rich-get-richer phenomenon.

I am not trying to say that luck alone determines success, but merely that dependency can hugely impact that level of success. In business, you might get a bit of publicity by, for example, being mentioned or interviewed by an influencer with a sizable audience. This publicity could have huge cascading repercussions. First, it may allow you to reach a large number of customers in a short amount of time. Second, due to dependency, other influencers are more likely to also mention or interview you because they see you as a known name. If you happen to have a good product or service, this whole process could exponentially grow your business.

This example is consistent with our previous discussion on risk-taking in chapter 4: specifically, not being afraid of small losses and taking risks when harm is limited. You would probably like to expose yourself to potentially high-impact positive events such as positive publicity.

To summarize, *dependence* refers here to when one event modifies the conditional probability of another event. Dependence can play a significant role in almost every endeavor in our lives, so let's try to better understand and take advantage of it. One important consideration in managing dependency is how to update our views (i.e., our probability estimates) based on the available information. This is where Bayesian thinking can help.

BAYESIAN THINKING

On July 3rd, 1988, an airplane was detected in the sky in the vicinity of USS *Vincennes*, a US Navy warship. The crew had to quickly identify whether this was a military aircraft on the verge of attacking the ship or a civilian airplane simply following its route. The consequences of being wrong would be huge. Misidentify a military plane, and their ship may well be attacked. Misidentify a civilian airplane, and they may end up killing hundreds of innocent people on board. There were only moments to decide, and the warship crew was under immense pressure.

Luckily, most of the time, you and I are not making life-and-death decisions like this; nevertheless, this harrowing tale relates to some circumstances we do face in real life. In some cases, we must indeed act under uncertainty, and the consequences of choosing the wrong option could be significant. In other words, there are no safe options. This is in contrast to the discussions we had in previous chapters on the benefits of taking risks when the potential harm is insignificant. In those scenarios, we always had a safe or low-risk option.

In situations with no safe options, reducing uncertainty, even by a small amount, can be hugely beneficial. We may not be able to eliminate uncertainty, but given the high costs (or benefits) of taking particular options, we should strive to paint a picture that's as close to reality as possible. Based on the evidence and observations at hand, we should create the best probabilistic view or belief of a situation. Bayesian thinking can be immensely helpful in such situations.

You may be wondering what happened with the warship. The decision was made to fire two surface-to-air missiles, both of which, tragically, hit the civilian airliner, killing the 290 passengers and crew on board. I do not have the expertise on this matter to say whether this tragedy could have been avoided. Nevertheless,

Bayesian thinking can be immensely helpful in many such decision-making scenarios as it allows us to use available evidence to update our probabilistic beliefs about the world around us.

A PRACTICAL APPLICATION OF BAYES' RULE

Mathematically, Bayes' rule is very simple. If you have ever taken an introductory probability and statistics course, you have likely come across it. However, evidence shows that even when we are aware of this rule, we are not always good at applying it in our decision-making. Before we go into the details, let's start with a real story showing a simple but practical application of Bayes' rule.

An author I know does not like fame for personal reasons. Because of his aversion to fame, when he decided to write a book, he considered the possibility that it could become too popular; say, a bestseller in its category. My question is this: Should he have bothered worrying about that? This is where Bayes' rule comes in to help.

Here is an interpretation of Bayes' rule that I have always found useful and intuitive. You start with some initial belief, usually called your *prior probability* or *base rate*:

Initial (Prior) Probability = Base Rate

Then, you update your estimated probability based on the evidence or information at hand. You can do this by multiplying your initial probability by an *evidence factor*:

Updated Probability = Base Rate × Evidence Factor

Let's see how we can apply this interpretation of Bayes' rule to my author friend. In his scenario, the base rate is the probability of a random book becoming famous; we can quantify this as the percentage of famous books among all published books. This, of course, depends on how you define *famous book*, but even with the most generous definition, a simple calculation shows that this probability is well below 1 in 10,000. That is our initial belief, our base rate.

Now, we need to update this initial belief with any other information we might have. In this case, the information could come from the quality of his book. For the purposes of this example, allow me to grossly overestimate his talent. Let us say his talent is so great that the chance of his book becoming famous is 20 times that of the average book in its genre.

In this case, the number 20 is the *evidence factor*, which I'll use to update his probability of fame. The probability of him becoming famous is obtained by multiplying the base rate by the evidence factor: 1/10,000 × 20. This gives us the updated probability of fame of 2 in 1,000. My conclusion is that even with such generous calculations, he should not worry about fame as a consequence of publishing his book.

Interestingly, thinking through this exercise has also helped me in writing my own book. The base rate reminded me that almost all books have relatively few readers. Knowing that my book will in all likelihood *not* be a famous book, I could simply focus on doing the best job I could of writing a useful and enjoyable text without being distracted by unlikely possibilities. I hope that a solid group of readers will find this book useful, but I will not be surprised if the number of readers is very small.

DO NOT FORGET THE BASE RATE (THE PRIOR PROBABILITY)!

To apply Bayes' rule to our decision-making, we need two things: an initial belief (base rate) and an evidence factor. Psychologists have observed that, quite often, we fail to appropriately account for the base rate. That is, in day-to-day life, we tend to attribute too much weight to the evidence factors and underestimate the effect of the base rate. This is sometimes referred to as *base-rate neglect.*[11]

For example, say I want to start a company and would like to evaluate my success probability. The base rate here could be the average success rate of start-ups in my industry, which is likely a low percentage. However, I might focus too much on the strengths of my start-up idea and my team's talent, which may lead me to overestimate my success probability and neglect to fully recognize the impact of the low base rate. Instead, I should multiply the low base rate (the average success rate in my industry) by the evidence factor (the fact that I have a great idea and a good team).

Of course, this alone does not mean that I should not start the company. It might simply mean that I need to do proper risk management, for example, by using the techniques discussed in chapters 4 and 5.

Moreover, the argument against beginning a start-up may also fall prey to a *fixed-mindset trap*: It is true that the base rates for start-up successes are usually low. Most start-ups do fail. Nevertheless, assigning a fixed probability to your start-up might be misleading and counter-productive. As we've discussed, persistence could amplify

11 If you'd like to learn more about this topic, Daniel Kahneman provides an insightful discussion on the base-rate neglect phenomenon in his (very famous!) book *Thinking, Fast and Slow.*

your success probability. This persistence can be applied to your start-up and any subsequent ones you might found or join. Many entrepreneurs continue to adapt and try different paths; if their current venture fails, they'll start a new one. As previous chapters demonstrated, the probability of such entrepreneurs eventually succeeding is much higher than the simple base rate for a single start-up.[12]

BAYES HELPS US WORRY LESS!

I have personally found Bayes' rule very helpful in removing worries from my life, thus improving my well-being. Many of the things we might worry about on a daily basis are unlikely to occur, but we might not realize it due to the base-rate neglect phenomenon.

Let's say my wife has taken my kids to an event, they are late coming home, and she doesn't answer her phone when I call. My automatic reaction in such a scenario might be to worry. Could they have been in an accident? Might a freak storm have hit the event? A simple look at our previous discussions on Bayes tells me that an accident or freak storm is very unlikely, as the base rate is quite low. The much likelier scenario is something benign like the fact that my kids did not want to leave the event, and my wife's phone is on silent mode. The base rate for this harmless scenario is much higher than it is for the disaster scenarios! This thinking can be quite useful when used as a complement to proper risk management.

Through Bayesian thinking, I have reduced my worries significantly. I try to avoid taking stupid risks, I take

12 Carol Dweck provides useful discussions on fixed and growth mindsets in her book *Mindset*.

precautions, and I do not worry about the rest. Many of the things I might otherwise worry about are very unlikely to actually occur.

THE STICKY PRIOR PROBLEM

So far, we have mostly discussed scenarios in which we tend to ignore or undervalue the base rate and focus too closely on the evidence. But let me ask you a question: Can you think of an example of a scenario in which we often put too much weight on the prior belief and not enough on the evidence?

One such scenario is when the issue is somehow tied to our identity such as political affiliation. For example, if some damaging evidence about a party that we support comes to light, we are much more likely to dismiss or rationalize it and stick to our prior belief about said party than to update our belief with outside evidence.[13]

For me, the practical takeaway is that I have to be very careful about things that I associate with my identity. When it comes to unimportant things—say, which political party I support—I make sure that I do not make them a part of my identity. On other hand, when it comes to more fundamentally important issues in life—say, which sports team I support—you bet I will make sure they are tied to my identity.

THE SIMPLE MATH OF BAYES' RULE

We've already looked at an intuitive formula for Bayes'

13 Lisa Bolton and Americus Reed's original research on the extent to which identity influences our beliefs is very insightful. Furthermore, Adam Grant (in Think Again), Annie Duke (in Quit), and Julia Galef (in The Scout Mindset) provide illuminating discussions on this phenomenon.

rule, but the math behind this rule is also quite simple; it just involves working with percentages. Let's get the math conversation over with quickly so that we can continue with the more practical stuff.

Say you would like to update your prior belief about a hypothesis H given some evidence E. Note that I use the word *hypothesis* broadly here. It can refer to anything we are uncertain about: some event in the past or future, an unproven fact, or anything else. Bayes' rule itself is very general and can be applied to anything, including medical diagnoses, legal cases, business analytics, and personal beliefs.

I claim that you already know Bayes' rule, even if you think you don't. Don't believe me? I can prove to you that I'm right using the following example.

Consider a population of people. For the sake of this example, let's say roughly half of them are male and half are female. You are interested in finding the probability of a randomly chosen person being very tall. Specifically, we define a person as *very tall* if their height is above the threshold of six feet. Suppose you know that in this population, 20% of males and 10% of females are very tall. Thus, as shown in figure 6.1, on the whole, about 15% of the population is very tall. This 15% is your base rate, or prior probability, before observing any data about a particular person.

Now comes the observation or evidence E. A random person from the population is chosen, and you are informed that this person is a man. What is the probability that this person is very tall? If you said 20%, congratulations—you understand Bayes' rule. You updated

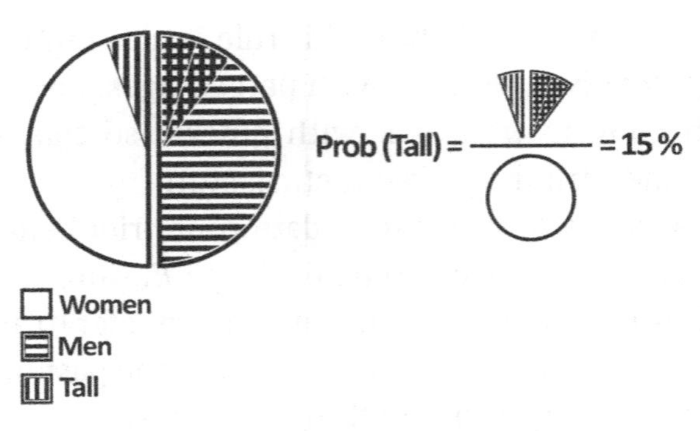

Figure 6.1. Finding the base rate. A prior probability, or base rate, is obtained by finding the percentage of tall people in the population.

your base rate of 15% to 20% after receiving the extra information that the person is a man. In this problem, the hypothesis *H* refers to the chosen person being very tall, and the observation or evidence *E* is that the chosen person is a man. See figure 6.2.

This example illustrates an intuitive method for applying Bayes' rule: imagine a large population, and look at the numbers or percentages in any category you're interested in.

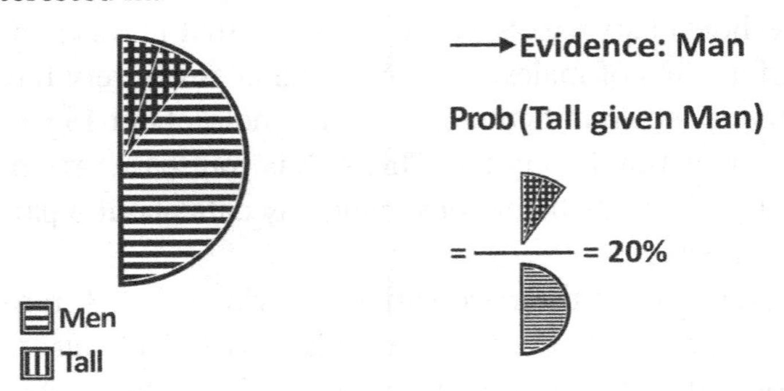

Figure 6.2. A pictorial illustration of updating a probability given evidence. Given that a randomly chosen person is a man, the probability of him being tall is obtained by the portion of tall men among all men.

Now, here is a different question: If you are informed that a random person from the same population is very tall, what is the probability that the person is a man?

While considering this problem, you may notice a certain symmetry. Essentially, there are two attributes on which we categorize the population: sex and height. If we observe one attribute, we can update our probability of the other attribute. We conclude that the second problem is very similar to the first one. We can approach the second problem as follows:

Consider a population of 1,000, 500 of whom are male and 500 of whom are female. Since 20% of males are very tall, we have 100 very tall men in this population; since 10% of females are very tall, we have 50 very tall females. In other words, two-thirds of the very tall people are men. As figure 6.3 shows, since our only evidence in this case is that the chosen person is very tall, we conclude that our updated probability of the person being a male is now two-thirds or about 67%.

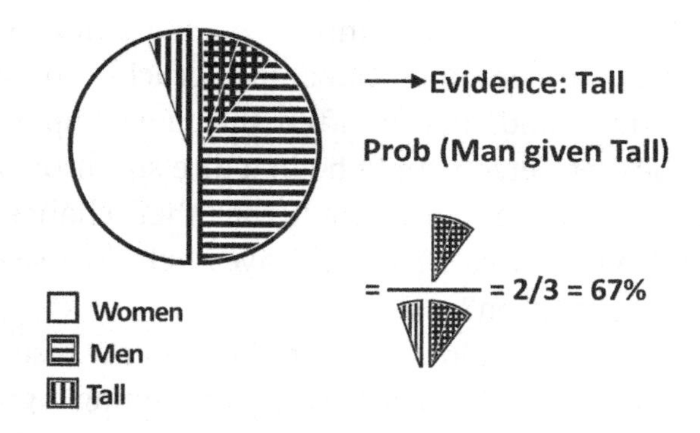

Figure 6.3. Another intuitive way of applying Bayes' rule. Given that a randomly chosen person is tall, the probability that he or she is man is given by the portion of men among all tall people.

Note that this 67% also makes intuitive sense. Remember, your prior probability or base rate was 50% probability for male, but because the percentage of very tall males is higher than the percentage of very tall females, your observation that the person is very tall amplifies the probability of the person being male.

So there it is: Bayes' rule. Just think of probabilities as percentages, then work out the percentage in the category consistent with your observation or evidence.

HOW TO FIND A LOST PERSON

For more than 18 years, the body of a climber known only as Green Boots lay near the top of Mount Everest in plain view of other mountaineers. Many climbers encountered his body during their expeditions. In fact, it is estimated that around 200 corpses remain on Everest.

We frequently hear stories of mountain climbers or hikers who are lost or injured due to snow, avalanches, failing GPSs, animal encounters, or something else. Search and rescue operations are crucial in such circumstances, and time is often the most important factor. The lost person could be in a dire situation, and the sooner they are found, the higher their chances of survival. Now, how can Thomas Bayes help in a search and rescue operation?

A few years ago, along with students in my research group, I worked on a project involving sending a group of drones to fly over a designated area and search for a lost person. These drones could use cameras and other sensors to detect the person. A crucial aspect of building the system was programming the paths the drones should take. Which area should be searched first and through which path?

A key part of the search algorithm is, therefore, the *probability map* of the region—a map that indicates the probability of the lost person being in each region. We begin with an initial belief about the possible locations of the target (i.e., the lost person). Then, as the drones fly over the area, the probability map is updated based on the drones' observations. Bayes' rule is used at each stage to update the probabilities.

Indeed, Bayes' rule is crucial here: it gives us the updated probability map. Combining the probability map with the location and energy constraints, the drones could choose their next move to minimize the search time. Yes, among other things, Bayes' rule can save lives.

HOW TO CHOOSE OUR PRIORS: ENTROPY AND RISK CONSIDERATIONS

When you want to apply Bayes' rule to your own life, you'll need to start with a base rate, your initial belief on a subject. Sometimes, figuring out the base rate is quite straightforward. Say a doctor wants to assess the probability of a patient having a disease based on evidence such as symptoms and test results. The base rate could simply be the prevalence of the disease among the group the patient belongs to. Such statistics are usually available.

In other situations, finding the base rate is not so straightforward. In fact, your initial belief could be subjective; different people could have different prior beliefs (also known as priors). When faced with such scenarios, I personally follow two guidelines to establish my prior belief.

PRIOR'S FIRST GUIDELINE: ENTROPY

My first guideline for choosing a prior is based on our discussion from chapter 3 on maximum entropy or, more generally, the minimum assumption approach (MAA). One interesting aspect of the Bayesian approach relates to that discussion. Remember, we often overestimate our knowledge and the accuracy of our assumptions on any subject. This was the starting point for us to develop the MAA. Let us now connect that discussion with the Bayesian approach.

Essentially, the MAA tells us that we should gravitate toward a prior probability with higher uncertainty. Then, as we gain more evidence, we can update our probabilities and reduce our uncertainty. In other words, when you are deciding between two hypotheses, the closer you make your initial probabilities to 50%, the higher amount of uncertainty you are assuming in your prior belief.

PRIOR'S SECOND GUIDELINE: RISK CONSIDERATION

My second guideline for establishing a prior belief is based on risk management: I want to make sure I do not underestimate the risk of negative outcomes in my decision-making. To accomplish this, I intentionally *over*estimate the probability of a hypothesis with significant negative consequences. For example, in an earlier discussion where we considered fame as a potential negative outcome for my author friend, I intentionally overestimated the prior probability to be 1 in 10,000. I did the same thing when I was estimating the weight of his talent (the generous evidence factor of 20).

In that case, even with such overestimations, the resulting probability of that risky outcome of fame was small, which was comforting to know. Granted, fame is not a catastrophic outcome. However, we can apply the same overestimation procedure when we the probabilities of truly catastrophic outcomes.

EXPLOITING PROBABILISTIC BELIEFS: THE UNCERTAINTY MINDSET

Before we move on to the next topic, I would like to include a somewhat different discussion from the rest of the book. First, a warning: this discussion is very personal and highly subjective. I would like to share with you how I personally use an idea that I refer to as *probabilistic beliefs* or *the uncertainty mindset*. I completely understand that many readers may not want to apply such an approach to their personal beliefs. Nevertheless, since I have personally benefited from such an approach, allow me to present a brief story.

Shortly after my fifteenth birthday, I "discovered" that I was wiser than most other people on the planet. (What? Like you never had any stupid ideas when you were a teenager?) Luckily, that phase of life did not last very long, and I have (hopefully) more or less come to my senses. During that episode, I became fascinated by fundamental questions about the meaning of life, morality, ethics, and so on. However, I did not read much philosophy. In fact, it was only recently that I took a major step toward becoming a philosopher: I grew a beard.

Nevertheless, those fundamental questions never left my thoughts. I finally discovered how helpful the "uncertainty mindset" can be in formulating my personal approach to life. In a moment, I will focus on the free-will debate and discuss how I personally benefit from a probabilistic belief approach. Before that, let's discuss the general idea.

MAIN IDEA: TAKING ADVANTAGE OF UNCERTAINTY

In the Bayesian approach, we need to start with a prior belief: our initial belief about a subject. As you know, the minimum assumption approach (MAA) suggests we should gravitate toward a prior with higher uncertainty. As we gain evidence, our uncertainty is reduced, and we update our probabilities.

Now, combining the Bayesian approach with this approach to the priors results in an interesting conclusion: some level of uncertainty almost always remains. In other words, we are rarely 100% sure about anything. We are usually OK with this. But can we somehow take advantage of this uncertainty?

This is not a trivial question. On the surface, the more information you have, the better you are able to make decisions. Or are you? This is where I like to use the *probabilistic belief approach*. The basic idea is this: When we can assume we have a certain level of uncertainty about a subject, we have the freedom to focus on the beneficial aspects of every possibility. It's kind of like having your cake and eating it too!

In the following section, I will provide an example to illustrate this using the free-will debate. Caution! This example will get a bit philosophical.

HOW I PERSONALLY EXPLOIT THE FREE-WILL DEBATE

Do we really have free will? This is a question as old as time and a challenging one to answer. The answer depends on what we mean by *free will* and might involve a discussion on consciousness, fate, the laws of the universe, and so on. But, with the Bayesian view in mind, we can look at this question in a different way.

Without bothering ourselves with a difficult discussion on free will, consciousness, and other such philosophical concepts, we could instead take a probabilistic view. There is a chance that the free-will hypothesis is true and a chance that it is not true. Therefore, we have two hypotheses: the no-free-will hypothesis, and the free-will hypothesis. How does this affect us practically? Here is how I personally benefit from the uncertainty regarding these hypotheses.

THE NO-FREE-WILL HYPOTHESIS: I HATE NO ONE!

If the no-free-will hypothesis is true—if we are entirely products of our genes, our environments, and outside forces—our investigation has an interesting conclusion: the no-free-will view could be used to amplify our compassion toward others. I cannot really hate anyone if I believe they have no free will. Even if a person is truly evil, they are evil mainly as a result of their genes, their past, and their environment. They cannot be blamed.

Given that there is a nonzero probability that the no-free-will hypothesis is true, I am able to free myself of animosity toward any person (well, almost), no matter how evil they might appear to me. I find this stance very helpful for my personal happiness and well-being. I notice that as I grow older, this no-hate attitude has become stronger. I feel much more compassionate toward others, even those who have somehow harmed me.

FREE-WILL HYPOTHESIS: ACCOUNTABILITY AND RESPONSIBILITY!

Now, let's consider the case where the free-will hypothesis is true. From this perspective, it is much easier to identify how we can benefit.

We all experience a considerable group of useful feelings and emotions that help us build a better society, and it seems to me that assuming some level of free will helps to justify those feelings. We like people who are generous, altruistic, and kind; when someone is kind to us, we generally like to reciprocate. This, indeed, helps generate the cooperation, friendships, and love that make up significant parts of our well-being.

The free-will hypothesis can easily support and warrant all of these good feelings. As before, since I assume a nonzero probability for this hypothesis, it is much easier for me to freely enjoy my useful feelings without concerning myself with whether they make sense from a narrow, strictly logical point of view.

THE UNCERTAINTY MINDSET STRATEGY

To sum up my probabilistic view of the free-will question, by assuming some uncertainty about the level of free will that humans might have, I can emphasize the beneficial aspects of each hypothesis.

I have been able to apply this view to my beliefs regarding different aspects of life, and I think I have benefited immensely from this approach. Adopting such a mindset has allowed me to have an easygoing approach to life and find uncertainty very pleasing. Part of life's beauty is found in its uncertainty, the mysteries, and the unknown, and I strive to benefit from this uncertainty as much as I can.

Remember, this last section was very subjective. It was not a scientific, logical, or deeply philosophical discussion on free will, psychology, or evolution; I simply view the probabilistic belief approach as a practical way of thinking, and I wanted to share something I found personally useful. (Please don't hate me if you found it stupid or unhelpful—after all, I might not have free will!)

In any case, as we will discuss in the following chapter on AI, I believe this uncertainty mindset can also help us free ourselves from judging other people. This freedom from a judgmental outlook comes from the humility that is the direct result of appreciating uncertainty.

Now, let's wrap up this personal discussion and turn to the final topic of this chapter, another aspect of dependency we can think of as *dependency of beliefs and actions*.

SEEKING ADVICE AND GROUP DECISIONS

Every year, the National Science Foundation (NSF) grants billions of dollars to support the progress of science. The agency invites researchers onto their panels to judge the quality of grant proposals, and the reviewers of those grants submit their proposal reviews before the panel. Significantly, reviewers cannot see other reviews until they submit their own. This is clearly a good practice because it ensures that reviewers make their reviews independently from others. You can easily guess what would happen if this guideline were not enforced: the earlier reviews could influence later reviews.

With this in mind, let's briefly discuss dependency of beliefs and actions through the lens of uncertainty. Specifically, let's discuss two distinct scenarios in which hiding information (or, equivalently, increasing uncertainty) can be helpful in our decision-making.

GROUP DECISIONS AND GAINING USEFUL ADVICE

First, hiding information is useful in collaborative scenarios such as the NSF panels discussed above. For example, say you would like to seek some advice on a situation. The best way to solicit unbiased advice is to describe the situation in the most objective way possible, without interjecting your personal opinion on the matter. Annie Duke describes this point perfectly in her book *How to Decide*.

As simple as this may seem, I have often failed to remain objective in these instances. Looking back at many of my past discussions, I realized that my main motivation behind consulting with someone else has often been to affirm their approval of my decision, not really to get their independent opinion. After finally noticing this and adjusting my methods to match those of Annie Duke's, I have discovered that the advice I have gotten from people has become much more useful.

COMPETITIVE SCENARIOS, BUSINESS, POLITICS, AND SPORTS

The second scenario where increasing uncertainty can help in terms of dependent actions is in competitive situations such as politics, business, and sports. The study of game theory looks at interactions among rational agents who usually compete for something, say, winning a game. Of course, this relates to many real-life situations such as politics, the military, business, and sporting events.

One of the most practical lessons we can learn from game theory is that randomness and uncertainty can be effectively utilized in many strategies for dealing with competitive situations. One danger in these competitive scenarios is that we might become too predictable, enabling our opponents to counter our actions with ease. In such scenarios, adding a bit of randomness creates unpredictability, which could be necessary in competitions.

Examples of such situations are abundant in sports; if you are a sports fan, I am sure you can easily name a few. However, game theory also has business applications. For example, businesses almost always maintain some level of uncertainty about their sales strategy, whether that's in terms of timing, the level of offered discounts, or the items on sale. If there is no uncertainty about sales, customers could easily predict the business's strategy and adjust their purchasing decisions accordingly, and the company's profit would be significantly reduced. As another example, the police can use randomization when setting up speed traps. If speed traps were deterministic in terms of time and location, they would be ineffective, as drivers would know when to reduce their speed to avoid a ticket. Here again, unpredictability helps.

So, if you are in a competitive scenario and find that your opponents frequently defeat you, it might be a good idea to check whether your predictability is a contributing factor. If this is the case, injecting some randomness into your strategy could potentially help you win.

CHAPTER TAKEAWAYS

- Dependence is a key issue in dealing with uncertainty. An important aspect of dependence is how earlier events can change the probability of other events.
- Dependence can cause network effects, nonlinearity, and heavy-tailed environments. In such situations, convergence laws (such as the law of large numbers) are not very helpful.

- Viral phenomena including viruses, viral videos, and popular songs are examples of the dependence effect.
- The dependence effect can partly explain the rich-get-richer phenomenon: each success can increase the probability of the next success, sometimes creating wild deviations in the distribution of wealth.
- In many scenarios, there are no safe options. In such situations, reducing uncertainty could significantly help in our decision-making. Bayes' rule, which gives us a systematic way to update our beliefs based on observations and evidence, could be helpful in these circumstances.
- An initial belief is usually referred to as prior probability or base rate. One way to apply Bayes' rule is to multiply the prior probability by an evidence factor to obtain the updated belief.
- Psychologists have observed that we tend to downplay the base rate and put too much emphasis on the evidence. Being aware of this tendency can help us obtain a more accurate picture in uncertain situations.
- One important application of Bayes' rule is in a scenario where the base rate is very small (say, the hypothesis that a catastrophic accident has occurred). In such scenarios, even if there is evidence in favor of the hypothesis (say, your loved one not answering the phone), the updated probability is still usually very small.

- The above point can potentially be used to reduce anxiety and worry, which can be a powerful complement to proper risk management.
- Another important scenario is when the base rate for success is small (say, entrepreneurship). Two actions might help in such scenarios: First, as discussed in previous chapters, we can appropriately manage our risk. Second, we can avoid a fixed mindset in which we focus too much on the small base rate by noticing that the odds of success can increase with persistence and more effort. Lessons learned from each failed venture could be used to increase our probability of success for the next one, as could increasing our number of attempts.
- There are also scenarios in which we tend to put too much weight on our initial belief and not enough weight on the evidence. A prominent example is when the issue relates to our identity.
- The math behind Bayes' rule can be made very intuitive and simple: we can think of probabilities as percentages, then work out the percentage in the category of interest consistent with our observation or evidence.
- Choosing the prior (base rate) can be tricky and subjective. I personally use two guidelines: (1) gravitate toward higher entropy and (2) overestimate the probability of unfavorable outcomes.
- I have personally benefited from a probabilistic belief system. When I assume a certain level of uncertainty on a subject, I have the freedom to focus on the beneficial aspects of each possibility.

- In the beginning stages of collaborative decision-making, dependency could be harmful. It is most helpful if group members first provide their opinions without being influenced by the opinions of others. Similarly, when asking for advice, we will get the most useful results if we ask our questions in the most neutral way possible without indicating our own opinion first.
- In competitive scenarios including business, politics, and sports, injecting a bit of randomness into our strategy could help our chances of success by preventing our competitors from easily predicting our actions.

CHAPTER 7: AI AND DECISION-MAKING

When Julie noticed the email in her inbox—the one she had been anticipating for months—she quickly opened it. She couldn't believe what she saw: she had been denied admission to her dream university. She was right to be shocked. After all, she had already been admitted to all the other top universities in the country. Julie is one of those outliers, the high-achieving type of student that top universities strive to attract. Here's the mystery: Why was Julie rejected?

As it turns out, the answer to Julie's mystery lies in AI. I have changed her name, but Julie's story is a real story. In this chapter, as we explore how AI works, we'll come to understand what happened to Julie, along with many more weird things about AI. Don't worry—it will be fun! In fact, one fundamental aspect of our understanding of AI will come through an old cartoon character.

Now, why are we focusing on AI? The answer is threefold. First, whether we like it or not, more and more predictions and decisions are being made by AI rather than humans. Thus, we humans can all benefit from an understanding of AI. Second, we can look at AI through the lens of uncertainty and randomness, which nicely relates to the topics we've looked at throughout this book.

Third, as AI tries to mimic natural intelligence, any concept we need to understand in order to learn about AI usually has a corresponding real-life concept. We will try to use these analogies and parallels to discuss our decision-making. This approach comes with two advantages: it makes AI easier to understand, and it helps us apply lessons from the world of AI to our everyday decision-making.

Great! Now, let's dig in.

WHAT IS MACHINE LEARNING (ML)?

The term *artificial intelligence* (AI) can be used broadly to mean many things. For the purposes of this book, I use AI to mean *machine learning* (ML). So what is machine learning? The following definition is often attributed to Arthur Samuel, a pioneer in the field of AI: "Machine learning is a field of study that gives computers the ability to learn without being explicitly programmed."

Basically, any time we collect data, we might be able to use ML to (1) discover patterns in the data and (2) teach the computer to complete tasks for us. For example, we might have an AI program that learns how to distinguish cats from dogs and categorize images accordingly. AI usually learns from examples, and as we will see, this process is not as magical as it might sound. Indeed, the basic ideas are simple.

ML VERSUS TRADITIONAL RULE-BASED COMPUTER PROGRAMS

Caution: if you are already familiar with ML, you may find the following few sections a bit boring! But don't worry; we'll get through them quickly and soon be on to the more interesting stuff.

Machine learning comes in a few different flavors, and here we'll focus on the supervised learning paradigm,[14] which I'll explain in a moment. First, let me ask you a question: How many centimeters is equal to one and a half meters? Since there are 100 centimeters in one meter, you would multiply 1.5 by 100 and logically conclude that 150 centimeters is equal to one and a half meters. Therefore, if I were to ask you to write a computer program to convert meters to centimeters, you would simply ask the program to multiply the input by 100, and the resulting output would be the correct answer.

Because we already know the rule needed for this program—multiply the input by 100 and return the resulting number—you would not need to use ML. The computer does not need to learn the rules because you're giving it the rules. See figure 7.1. Even if the rules were much more complicated, as long as we can write specific instructions to do the job, we most likely do not need ML.

---

14 One way to categorize general approaches to ML is as follows: (1) supervised learning, (2) unsupervised learning, and (3) reinforcement learning (RL). In supervised learning, the computer learns by examples. In unsupervised learning, the goal is usually to find patterns or structures in the input data. In RL, the computer usually learns by trying different strategies and experiences. Appendix B provides a brief introduction to these types of ML.

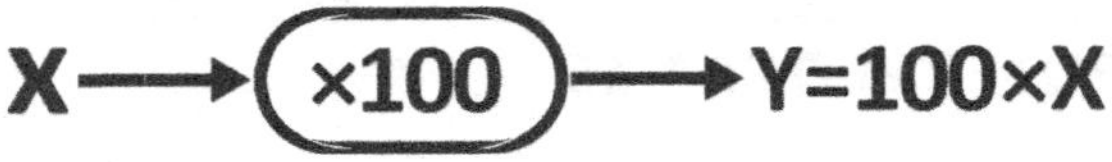

X → (×100) → Y=100×X

Figure 7.1. A traditional rule-based program. There is no need for ML here.

However, in some scenarios, we do not know the specific rules to procure a particular outcome. This may be because the problem is very complex, or there may be unknown factors that impact the output. For example, suppose you want to write a program that examines a medical image and determines whether the patient has a specific disease. Due to the complicated nature of the problem and the many variables involved that may differ from patient to patient, we may not know how to write specific mathematical rules for this problem like we did with the meter-to-centimeter conversion. In such scenarios, we could potentially use ML to *teach* computers to figure out the rules and return the result.

To do so, we would first obtain a large collection of images, some of which show patients with the disease and some of which show patients without the disease. From this set of images, the computer could learn how to detect the presence of the disease. This set of examples is called the *training data*. In supervised learning, training data is called *labeled data*, meaning we tell the computer what it is being shown by labeling each image. For example, an image is labeled as "one" when the patient does have the disease and "zero" when the patient does not.

We then feed this labeled data to an ML algorithm, and the algorithm tries to automatically learn the patterns associated with the disease. Of course, for the purposes of this chapter, we want to understand how this "learning" happens.

LEARNING ML FROM BARBAPAPA

Barbapapa was one of my favorite childhood cartoon series. The Barbapapas are shapeshifters, creatures who can physically change their bodies' shapes to suit a situation. They often do this to help others. Say there is heavy rain or a big storm; the family might change into the form of a big umbrella to protect others from the rain. When I was a kid, I used to imagine how amazing it would be if I could shapeshift.

As far as I know, we humans cannot shapeshift. However, ML structures can, and this shapeshifting ability is one of the main forces behind their power. To see this ability in action, let's get back to the meter-to-centimeter conversion problem we discussed earlier.

Remember, we did not need ML to solve that problem; we simply wrote the rule as $Y = 100 \times X$. Here, X (the length in meters) is the input of the program, and

Figure 7.2. An illustration of Barbapapa shapes based on the book *Barbapapa* written by Annette Tison and Talus Taylor, © Alice Taylor and Thomas Taylor and included by permission.

Y (the length in centimeters) is the output. In this way, a computer program can usually be thought of as a mathematical function or *mapping*: it takes a set of inputs *X* and maps those inputs to a set of outputs *Y*. The *Y* is what we would like to find out, and the rule that converts *X* to *Y* is our mapping.

Suppose that you write the following meters-to-centimeters program: when you enter a value for *X*, the program returns *Y*, which is 100 times *X*. In this case, you have essentially written a multiplier. But wait—there is nothing special about the number 100. You can replace this multiplicand (a number that is multiplied by another number) in your program with any other number to get a new program. For example, if you change the multiplicand to 12, you have a program that converts feet to inches. If you change it to 16, you have a program that converts pounds to ounces. The sky's the limit!

If we look at our program as a general multiplier with an *adjustable* parameter (the multiplicand), we are getting closer to the Barbapapa family's superpower of shifting to adjust to different situations. In this case then, we do not have just one program; as long as we give each program a different parameter, we effectively have many multiplier programs.

In sum, the first power of ML is the Barbapapa-like power to change according to the situation. We can achieve this flexibility by incorporating a set of adjustable or *tunable* parameters in our mapping or rule.

ML FLEXIBILITY: TUNABLE MAPPING OR BAG OF MAPPINGS

Here's another way to think about this flexibility. Each ML model consists of many mappings, each associated with a particular number assignment to the tunable parameters. During the training phase, the job of the ML algorithm is to choose the mapping suitable for the specific problem it is trying to solve. In our earlier example, a $Y = 100 \times X$ mapping is suitable for converting meters to centimeters, while a $Y = 16 \times X$ mapping would be suitable for converting pounds to ounces. We want our ML algorithm to choose the mapping that will give us the correct answer for the question we ask. (If we ask for three and a half meters in centimeters, we don't want the algorithm to use the pound conversion mapping!) Like the Barbapapa family, our algorithm should choose a suitable shape for each specific situation.

In other words, you can think of ML as a way to choose a specific mapping from a "bag of mappings." In

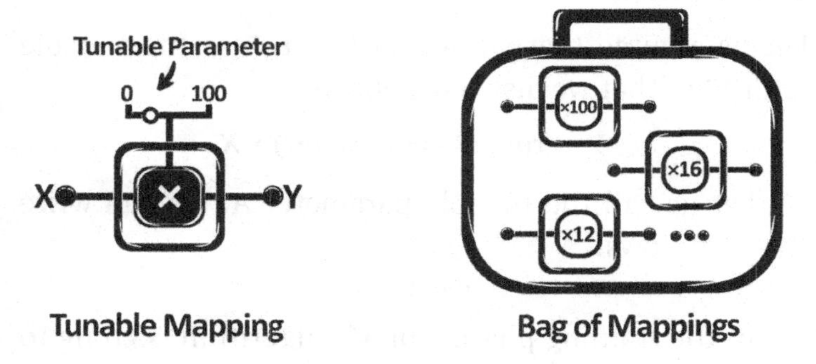

Figure 7.3. Two ways to think about machine learning. ML can be thought of equivalently as a tunable mapping or a bag of mappings. Training means you tune the tunable parameter. Equivalently, this means choosing a specific mapping from a bag of mappings.

this context, *learning* means choosing a particular mapping from our bag of mappings. Equivalently, as we see in figure 7.3, it also means adjusting the tunable parameters according to the desired task.

A SIMPLE EXAMPLE

Now that we have covered the concept of these "shape-shifting" tunable mappings, we can describe the machine learning process. To make sure the concept is clear, allow me to present a simple example before moving to more complex scenarios.

Let's assume that we do not know the rule for pound-to-ounce conversion, and we want to build an ML algorithm that learns this rule. We have two scales: one gives us the weight of an object in pounds, and the other gives us the weight in ounces. We will use these two scales in our learning process.

THE ML MODEL

Let us assume that we would like to use the tunable multiplier that we discussed above:

$$Y = (\textbf{tunable parameter}) \times X$$

Let us call the tunable parameter A. We can write this as follows:

$$Y = A \times X$$

In the training phase, our ML algorithm is going to "learn" the value of A. For simplicity, let us assume that our bag of mappings comes with only a limited set of values that A can possibly be. Specifically, let us assume

A comes in increments of 5, so the possible values for A are the following:

$$0, 5, 10, 15, 20, \ldots$$

This equation $Y = A \times X$, along with the set of choices for A, is referred to as our *machine learning model.*

COLLECTING DATA

We also need to collect some data, which we'll use to train our model on. To do this, we go and weigh some objects using our two scales. These scales are probably not very accurate, but they give us approximate weights in pounds and ounces. The training data is given in pairs made up of a pound value and its ounce counterpart, so they look like the following:

$$(1.4, 22.2), (3.2, 50.6), (2.1, 33.0), \ldots$$

The pairs have the following form: (X, Y) = (pounds, ounces). That is, the first number (X) is the weight in pounds, and the second (Y) is the weight in ounces. The second number, Y, is the label.

LEARNING = TRAINING = FITTING

Next, we start the learning process. Of course, in real life, this is done automatically by the algorithm. But let's slow it down and take a look at what's actually happening inside the algorithm. Since this is a simple model, we only have one tunable variable: A. Thus, learning simply boils down to adjusting the value of A. We need to choose a value for A that is most compatible with the training data. This means we want an A value that, when we plug it into our model, gives us results close to the data pairs (X, Y) in the training data. A value of A that is compatible with our training data is said to *fit* the training data.

Of course, we don't yet know what value of A will best fit our model to the data, so we start with an initial guess about the value of A—say, 5. So the mapping becomes as follows:

$$Y = 5 \times X$$

Then, we use the X values from the training data—1.4, 3.2, 2.1, etc.—to obtain the corresponding values of Y for this mapping. For example, let's take the data pair (1.4, 22.2) and try the X value in this mapping. For X = 1.4, we obtain the following:

$$Y = 5 \times 1.4 = 7$$

Now we compare the output, 7, to the label from the training data, 22.2, and see that this value is far from what we were expecting. That means this mapping is not a good fit; the value of A cannot be 5. Because we have both pieces of the data pair, we are able to tell the algorithm that its output is wrong and that it needs to change A. We increase A by one increment of 5, giving us $A = 10$.

This time, when we check, we see that our mapping, $Y = 10 \times X$, gives us values closer to the correct labels. This is encouraging. To get even closer, we increase A by another increment of 5, which gives us $A = 15$. This time, we really get excited because our mapping, $Y = 15 \times X$, gives values very close to the correct Ys:

$$Y = 15 \times X: (1.4, 21), (3.2, 48), (2.1, 31.5), \ldots$$

We want to see if we can get even closer to the correct labels, so we try the next value of A; now, $A = 20$. However, this time, we discover that we are now further from the correct labels (i.e., our error increases). It seems that $A = 15$ gives us the best fit: of all the options we tried, $A = 15$ brings us closest to the expected label.

While this was a very simple example, it should suffice to give a general idea of how supervised learning works. Remember, we can do *supervised learning* when we have labeled training data to compare results against; these labels allow the model to recognize when the mapping is wrong. (*Unsupervised learning* is done with unlabeled training data and goes a different route, which is briefly explained in Appendix B.)

We can search for the suitable values of the adjustable parameter A in an efficient way using methods such as *gradient descent*. We will not worry about the details of gradient descent in this book as the concept is not necessary for our discussion on ML (although it is an interesting topic on its own). Just think of it as a way to automatically search for suitable values of the adjustable parameters to better fit the training data. In other words, it is a way to select an appropriate mapping from our bag of mappings.

EXTENSION TO MORE REALISTIC ML

As I noted, the above pound-to-ounce conversion example was very simple. But while real-life ML models usually consist of much more sophisticated mathematical mappings with many adjustable parameters, the basic idea is typically the same.

Let's go back to the disease detection problem from earlier in the chapter. Here, the input X is an image, and the output Y can take one of two possible values: disease (1) or no disease (0). This type of problem is called a *classification problem* since the input images need to be classified into one of the possible groups (in this case, disease or no disease).

We might use an artificial *neural network* (*neural net* for short) for this problem. In essence, a neural net is just a type of tunable mapping that can have many adjustable parameters. In the training phase, the tunable parameters are adjusted to find the best fit for the training data. These adjustable parameters can be further fine-tuned as more data is observed, meaning the learning process can continue and improve if we obtain new data. Thus, AI can continue to learn as it accumulates more experience.

THE POWER OF ML

Let's pause here for a second. So far, we have looked at supervised ML as an adjustable mapping (equivalently, a mapping selected from a bag of possible mappings). This does not seem earth-shattering. Indeed, this idea of tunable mappings is very old. So why is ML powerful?

The power of ML comes from some important developments:

1. Big data: With more training data, you can use bigger ML models with a lot of adjustable parameters, so you get more powerful ML. It is not a coincidence that ML became more popular as

more data became widely available due to the expansion of the World Wide Web and other technological advancements.

2. Computing power: More computing power allows us to train bigger ML models with larger sets of training data in a shorter amount of time.
3. Better ML: Over the past few decades, researchers have developed more and more effective ML models and practices. This, of course, has led to performance improvement.
4. AI combinations: By combining simpler AIs, we can obtain more sophisticated systems capable of new tasks. For example, by using two neural networks and training them together in a specific way, we can obtain a generative adversarial network (GAN). From training data, GANs learn to generate new data that is similar to the original data. For instance, a GAN might learn to generate fake but realistic photos of human faces. The term *generative AI* is used to generally refer to AI models and algorithms that generate new content or data based on existing examples. The power of randomness, as discussed in this book, is crucial to generative AI. It plays a critical role in various stages, particularly in the generation process, where it enables the creation of diverse and novel outputs.

MODEL COMPLEXITY THROUGH A TRUE STORY

Now that we have reviewed the basic idea behind supervised machine learning, we are ready to discuss some important concepts. Let's set up a wine tasting competition scenario that will help us understand some of the traps and pitfalls ML can be prone to.[15]

THE WINE TASTING COMPETITION

The California State Fair Commercial Wine Competition plays a key role in promoting Californian wine across the US. Winning the competition brings recognition and could lead to an increase in sales for the local wineries. Given the business impact of the judges' decisions, wine judging is a potentially high-stakes and high-impact aspect of the competition. Understandably, it is important that the judges can be trusted to be consistent in their ratings.

Some years ago, several members of the state fair came up with a way to measure the consistency of the wine judging process. Since the wines presented during the competition are anonymized, the competition organizers decided to present some of the wines to the judges a second time. The judges assumed they were tasting all different wines when, in reality, they were occasionally tasting the same wines they'd already tried. The organizers could then measure any inconsistencies in scoring by comparing a judge's original score on a specific wine to their second

15 Robert T. Hodgson, "An Examination of Judge Reliability at a Major U.S. Wine Competition," *Journal of Wine Economics* 3, no. 2, 2008. The story was featured in the March 15, 2020, episode of *Choiceology* podcast with Katy Milkman.

score on that same wine.

They discovered that most of the judges were often inconsistent and scored the two samples of the same wine differently. However, about 15% of those judges exhibited a high level of consistency between the repeated wines. "Great! These are the good judges," the organizers thought. To be certain, they decided to repeat this experiment the following year with the same group of "good" and "bad" judges.

Here's a question for you: What do you think happened the following year? Before reading the rest of the story, think about your answer for a minute. Here's an even better question: Can you establish a connection to our ML discussion?

WHAT HAPPENED THE FOLLOWING YEAR

As you may have guessed, when the organizers repeated the experiment the following year, they found that a completely different group of judges replaced the previous group of "good" judges, and many of the good judges from the previous year ended up in the "bad" category.

To be fair, being a consistent wine judge is not an easy task. Many factors can affect a judge's decision, including sensory fatigue, time of day, order of tasting, and personal preference. The conclusion here is that in many cases, "good" judges were likely consistent only by chance. In essence, wine judging can be a very "noisy" process.

HOW DOES THIS RELATE TO ML?

I believe there is a lot we can learn about ML from this story. Let's return to our ML bag and apply some of this analogy. Suppose you have a large collection of mappings and a training data set, and you are trying to select the mapping that best fits your data.

You can think of each of the mappings as a wine tasting judge: you are trying to find the best judge—the one that is most consistent—from the group of judges. The list of wines that are repeated can be thought of as your training data. The correct label would be a score that's consistent for each repeated wine. For example, say we have a repeated 2022 Sonoma Zinfandel. If a judge gave that wine a score of 4.5 out of 5 both times, that's a correct label. If they scored it a 4 once and a 5 next, that's an incorrect label.

Using this list and the correct label, you select the best judges by separating out the judges who have applied the correct labels the most often. Similarly, in ML, we select the mapping that best fits the training data:

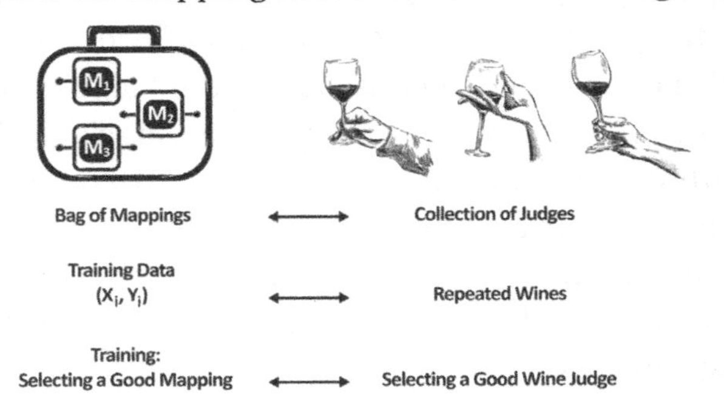

Figure 7.4. Collection of judges as a bag of mappings. This image shows the analogy: judge = mapping, repeated wines = training data.

that is, the one that minimizes the training error. This analogy is depicted in figure 7.4.

Using this analogy, let's discuss an important phenomenon in ML related to model complexity and overfitting. Remember, some judges or mappings perform well in the first round only by chance. In reality, they might not perform well in the next round. This is a fundamental point in our understanding of ML.

TRAINING VERSUS TESTING

The first lesson we learn here about ML is that simply training is not enough. With training alone, you might find that a particular mapping is a very good fit for your training data but performs poorly when tested on a new set of data. To address this issue, you have to perform testing: save some of your data for testing and call it your test set. Do not touch the test set during the training period. When training is done, use the test set to evaluate your mapping and ensure that it works well on the testing data. This can be done using what is usually referred to as cross validation.

In the context of our story, the first year's wine collection is the training set, and the following year's collection can be considered the test set. Many of the judges who performed well in the training set did not necessarily do well in the test set. This is an example of the important issue of *overfitting*, which occurs when we think our trained model is sound because it performs well on a particular data set, but then the model doesn't work on new data. That is, it only works well on the specific examples it was trained on.

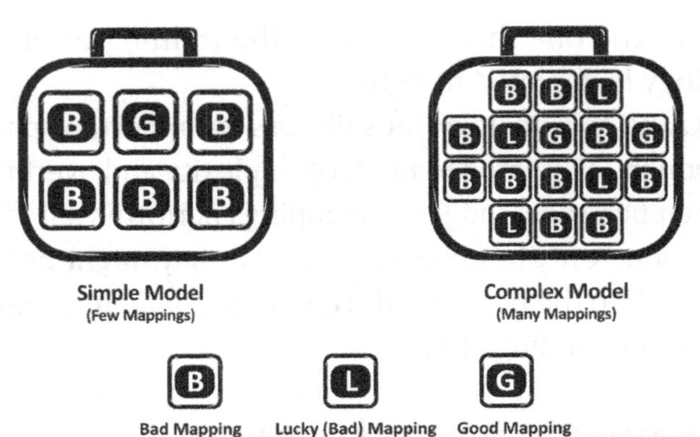

Figure 7.5. Bad and good mappings. Here we see a simple model (left) with a few mappings and a complex model (right) with many mappings.

OVERFITTING

To better understand how overfitting might occur in the wine judging scenario, let's consider the following questions: What is the probability that a judge scores repeated wines consistently by chance? What does this probability depend on?

Let's think about it this way. If I have a group of people, and I ask each of them to toss a coin 10 times, the chance of someone in the group obtaining 10 consecutive heads increases as the number of people increases. Similarly, if you have more judges, more judges will likely perform well by chance. Therefore, an important factor in answering the above questions is the number of judges.

The number of judges is equivalent to the number of mappings in your ML algorithm. Many mappings means a richer, more flexible model (or, equivalently, a more complex model). As depicted in figure 7.5, when you have a model with a lot of adjustable parameters, you most likely have a complex model.

As we use more complex models, two things happen:

1. It is more likely that a good mapping exists within your model that truly does what you want it to do.
2. It is more likely that many other bad mappings exist within your model that give you good results on the training data just by chance.

In the training phase, you might be fooled into choosing one of these bad mappings that performs poorly on other data. This is when overfitting occurs.

Thus, overfitting means that we are fitting to the noise, randomness, or idiosyncrasy of the training data, due to the high complexity and flexibility of our model. This is an undesired phenomenon and one of the most important trade-offs in ML.

In sum, higher flexibility can be both good and bad: good because flexibility makes it more likely that the model includes a good mapping, but bad because it increases the probability of overfitting.

BIAS-VARIANCE POINT OF VIEW

One closely related way of looking at model complexity and overfitting is through the lens of the *bias–variance trade-off*.

Let's say I have a thermometer that displays a temperature that is always two degrees lower than the real temperature. If the thermometer shows a temperature of 70°, the real temperature is 72°. In this context, we can say that our thermometer has a *bias* of -2°. Let's call this thermometer the *biased thermometer*.

Not satisfied with my thermometer, I buy a second thermometer, which is very volatile. Sometimes it shows one degree higher than the real temperature, sometimes three degrees lower, and so on. On average, it shows approximately the correct temperature, but it has high variation. Here, the issue is not bias but *variance*.

In the context of ML, simple models are like the first thermometer, while complex models are like the second one. That is, complex models usually have higher variance, while simple models have higher bias. Specifically, simple models have few tunable parameters, so there is not much variability in their results. If you train your simple model again with a different set of training data for your problem, the result will more or less be a similar mapping, so you will have more or less the same error rate as before. Thus, you could say simple models are consistent, but their accuracy might be off (high bias, low variance).

On the other hand, if you train your complex model again with a different set of training data for your problem, your result might show a completely different mapping. Complex models might be accurate on average but have high variability (low bias, high variance). In the end, performance is affected by both variance and bias. We need to find the sweet spot to avoid overfitting and underfitting.

SOME LESSONS FOR DECISION-MAKING

Overfitting can happen in contexts beyond ML and can have significant implications in life and business decision-making. Let's pause our discussion on machine learning to look at a few real-life lessons.

1. The power of simple solutions: An advantage of simple models is that they are less prone to overfitting. For example, remember the 1/N rule from chapter 3: if you have N assets, you can allocate your money equally between them, giving you a uniform allocation. In that chapter, we also introduced a relaxed version of the 1/N rule. We justified such approaches from the point of view of entropy and uncertainty. Our overfitting discussion provides another argument in favor of the 1/N rule and its variations: more sophisticated methods usually have high variance and suffer from overfitting, but the 1/N rule is much more robust.
2. Overthinking avoidance, early stopping, and satisficing: When faced with a decision involving high uncertainty, it is tempting to try to determine the best choice. However, due to a lack of information, this could result in "fitting the noise" rather than the signal, a phenomenon similar to overfitting in ML. In such situations, it might be beneficial to avoid overthinking and stop the decision-making process once you've come to a suitable decision. Satisficing, discussed in chapter 4, is a manifestation of this principle. In general, when there is high uncertainty and the stakes are relatively low, making a fast decision could save a lot of time and other resources.
3. Role of chance: Another takeaway from our

discussion on wine judging could help us avoid being fooled by randomness, as Nassim Taleb calls it. We saw that when there are many judges, it's likely that some of them are performing well just by chance. Similarly, in finance, where there are thousands and thousands of fund managers, some of them might have good results several years in a row simply by chance. It is very difficult to separate the roles of luck and skill in areas like finance. Personally, this reaffirms my fondness for simple investing strategies like buying mostly index funds and keeping the rest of my funds in low-risk assets such as checking or savings accounts or certificates of deposit (CDs).

Before moving on to more lessons, let's first discuss how to avoid overfitting and other ML pitfalls.

AVOIDING OVERFITTING

Based on our discussion so far, we can think of a few ways to mitigate overfitting:

1. More data: If you toss a coin five times, you might get lucky and get four or five heads, but if you toss the coin 20 times, it is extremely unlikely to get almost all heads. Similarly, if you have a bigger sample of repeated wines, it becomes less likely for each judge to obtain a good rating of consistency just by chance. So, as you get more training data, it becomes less and less likely that a mapping in your bag performs well by chance. Thus, more data usually means less chance of overfitting.

2. Regularization: Limit the complexity of our model as we discussed earlier in this section.
3. Cross validation: Randomly select a part of your data and keep it for testing.

So, are these three measures sufficient to create a mapping with satisfactory performance on new and unseen data? Unfortunately, as we will find, that is not the case.

AVOIDING SAMPLING OR SELECTION BIAS

Say you would like to build an AI that can detect whether or not a bird in a picture is a penguin. To accomplish this, you obtain a large collection of images carefully labeled as "penguin" or "non-penguin"; this is your training and test data. You take the three measures mentioned to avoid overfitting, and you observe very good results in both your training set and your test set. Can you be sure you have a good AI? Before reading the rest of this section, stop and think about the answer to this question.

Upon closer inspection, to your dismay, you discover that all your computer program is doing is distinguishing the color of the background. You look back at your data and notice that almost all of your penguin pictures have a background consisting of snow and ice, while your other birds have a green or brown background. Thus, your program has a reasonably low error rate in both the training set and the test set by simply classifying pictures based on the color of their background. If you give your program a new picture of a snow-covered backyard, the picture will be classified as a penguin, even if no penguins appear in the image. On the other hand, a picture of a penguin in a zoo with a brown background will be classified as a non-penguin.

Obviously, this is far from what you wanted. This issue can be thought of as a *sampling bias* problem: your sample collection of pictures did not have enough diversity in the backgrounds, so your sampling was biased toward pictures with a certain kind of background. Since this bias was present both in your training and test sets, cross validation did not prevent the problem. One way to address this problem is to make sure that your data, both training and test, include enough pictures with diverse backgrounds.

ML algorithms learn from the data you give them. If there is a bias in the data, that bias will be transferred to the AI. We have to be careful to prevent historical biases from creeping into our AI. Issues of bias become very important as reliance on AI increases in law enforcement, credit rating analysis, job candidate evaluation, and other areas.

In general, ML algorithms are susceptible to picking up unwanted correlations. Good results in the lab are encouraging, but good performance in real-world applications would be much more convincing. Indeed, dealing appropriately with subtleties such as overfitting, sampling bias, the curse of dimensionality, and data-snooping is an important skill for anyone working in ML.

A SHORT QUIZ ABOUT ENTREPRENEURSHIP

Now, allow the professor in me to test you with a quick quiz before continuing. Don't worry—you've got this!

Let's say you'd like to open a restaurant in your

town. First, you want to get an estimate of the average profitability of the restaurants in the area. Since yours is a small town, you know all the current restaurant owners, and they are willing to share information about their earnings with you. You crunch the numbers and find that on average, restaurants are indeed lucrative in your town.

Now, there are a couple of issues with this approach. Considering what we've discussed so far, can you tell me what, specifically, is wrong?

First, there is sampling bias here. The key phrase in my problem statement is "current restaurant owners." Successful restaurants stay in business for a long time; therefore, they have a much higher chance of being in business when you take your poll. On the other hand, less successful restaurants tend to go out of business more quickly and thus have a smaller chance of being in business at the time of your analysis. This means that you are probably overestimating the average profit of restaurants in your town. A better way of estimating the average profit might be to include in your sample all the restaurants that opened in the past 20 years, whether or not they are currently in business.

Another problem is that average profitability is probably not a good measure to use anyway. Why not? Because business ventures often belong to heavier-tailed environments, and as we have discussed in chapter 5, average values tend to be misleading in heavy-tailed environments. A few outliers, for example, could significantly magnify the average values. Say there are currently 10 open restaurants. Of those 10 restaurants, 9 break even, but 1 has a $10 million profit per year. In this case, the "average" profit would be $1 million per year. This is, of course, a misleading value for someone looking to open a restaurant. You are better off looking at the entire distribution and not paying too much attention to the average.

There are other issues here as well, some not directly related to the discussion in this chapter. I am guessing you have already thought of them and know them better than I do, especially if you have experience building businesses. My point is that sampling or selection bias is sometimes easy to miss if we are not careful.

How do we get better at spotting selection or sampling bias? One way is to ask ourselves what unseen data we are failing to consider. For example, we are all pretty good at spotting sampling bias when we watch testimonials companies provide on their websites. Obviously, the company is choosing to share only testimonials from happy customers. This is an example of obvious sampling or selection bias.

On the other hand, the selection bias in the restaurant question was a bit more subtle, and we only noticed it when we actively asked ourselves about the unseen data. Only then did we notice that we weren't considering all of the restaurants that went out of business.

AI DECISION-MAKING AND JULIE'S MYSTERY

Remember Julie's story from the beginning of the chapter? I heard her story from a colleague who is a professor at the university that denied Julie's admission. Let's solve this mystery. Here is what happened.

To improve its admission process, the university had hired an outside firm. One of the goals of this firm was to increase the university's *yield*. What is yield, and why did they want to increase it? Here, *yield* is defined as the percentage of students who choose to enroll in the university after having been accepted. This yield is used in college and university rankings, so the university had an incentive to increase it.

The outside firm developed an AI to help improve admission and increase the university's yield. However, it turned out the AI put too much weight on increasing the yield. The algorithm decided that top applicants such as Julie, who were likely to have received offers from elsewhere, were unlikely to enroll, so admitting them would lower the university's yield. Thus, the algorithm decided to deny them all! Luckily for Julie, this was discovered after she wrote to the university officials and asked for an explanation, and she was admitted.

This story is a reminder that we need to be careful when defining our "objective function" for an AI. AI does not have its own goals; we must define those goals explicitly. This is important during the learning process when different possible mappings are compared. If we are not careful, there will be discrepancies between our intentions for the AI and what it will actually do. To be fair, AI practitioners these days are usually cognizant of such issues, but it is always helpful to remind ourselves of such past mishaps.

PREDICTION MEANS REDUCING UNCERTAINTY

The word *prediction* is commonly used for machine learning tasks; however, the key goal can be expressed as *reducing uncertainty*. Specifically, a prediction—that is, a reduction of uncertainty—does not necessarily have to be about the future.

For example, let's say you want to find out if someone has committed tax fraud or not based on their tax paperwork. You might have historical data for many people who filed their taxes in previous years and information on whether any of their past filings were fraudulent. With this data, you might want to develop an ML program that computes the probability of tax fraud for the most recent tax period. Even though the fraud could have happened in the past, we might call this predicting because the goal is to reduce uncertainty about fraud. In this case, you might want to label Y as "plus one" if there is fraud and "minus one" if there is no fraud.

TAKING ADVANTAGE OF AI

By this point, we have made a herculean effort in discussing how ML works, its pitfalls, and some of its implications for decision-making. Now comes the fun part. How can we take advantage of AI? What is a good AI-inspired strategy in, say, business? How does AI impact the job market? How effective is

AI at decision-making? And what are the risks of AI decision-making?

Like any other technology, AI can change rapidly, so it is not always easy to predict long-term trends. To have a meaningful discussion on the above questions, we must go back to the basic features of today's ML algorithms. I'll try to discuss these important questions by touching on the limitations of current AI.

CURRENT AI, GPT, AND SOME LIMITATIONS

AI is truly incredible, but it also has some limitations that will be helpful to keep in mind as we figure out how to take advantage of it. Let's look at three important limitations of current AI systems that have critical implications: (1) limited understanding, (2) the slow change assumption, and (3) the tail problem.

ML methods come in different flavors, but our discussion on ML reveals that current ML is mainly concerned with identifying patterns in data and learning mathematical mappings that imitate how humans perform a certain task.

1. LIMITED UNDERSTANDING

Current AI does not understand concepts exactly like humans do; it often tries to imitate what it has seen in its training data. In other words, AI currently lacks the breadth and depth of human cognition.

Consider the field of robotics. For some physical tasks that are trivial for humans, it is notoriously hard to build robots that can adequately perform those tasks, partly due to the broad and open-ended nature of such tasks. Say you would like a maid robot that does your house chores for you. Due to the uncountable possible situations such a robot might encounter and the common-sense reasoning required to address them, designing a robot that can complete your house chores turns out to be challenging.

This discussion gives us a clue about the impact of AI on jobs in the near future. A likely scenario for changes in many professions is human and AI cooperation. This is one of the reasons that I think it is important for everyone to understand AI and its limitations and strengths. Even if you are not replaced with an AI application, you are likely to be working with AI soon if you don't already.

Of course, there have been significant and exciting developments in this field. For example, ChatGPT, launched in 2022 by OpenAI, is an AI chatbot seemingly capable of understanding human language and producing impressive text in response to questions on almost any subject. Other companies have also developed language models with similar capabilities to ChatGPT. The applications of such technologies could be unbounded.

However, at the time of this writing, even powerful language models such as ChatGPT do not really comprehend the concepts behind the text they produce. Impressive machine learning techniques have been used to make them powerful, but in essence, you can still think of them as the result of choosing a mapping from a huge bag based on an enormous amount of training data. They do not yet have the deep understanding and comprehensive critical thinking that humans can possess. Thus, users need to verify the information provided by GPT and similar systems.

As we will see in the following sections, this limitation could have important implications, for example, when we deal with sensitive, rare, or evolving scenarios. Of course, all of this might change as clever researchers continue to work on AI. It will be exciting to see how things evolve as AI progresses. For now, we do not yet have a good understanding of consciousness and how it might relate to intelligence at a deeper level. A breakthrough in this area would be amazing and could have significant implications and consequences.

One last note on this point: As I mentioned above, AI does not understand concepts the way humans do. Note the bias in this sentence. I am assuming that a human's particular way of understanding is somehow the ideal form of intelligence. However, it is possible that some other form of intelligence, such as AI, can be more effective than human intelligence. It is better for us to acknowledge this possibility and be prepared for it.

2. THE SLOW CHANGE ASSUMPTION

As we discussed, AI usually learns by discovering patterns in the data. This relies on two assumptions: First, patterns exist in the data. Second, the patterns are reasonably stable, or at least they change slowly enough for the AI to adapt as it observes new data. Statistically, for the AI to be effective, the future should resemble the past. This is related to the mathematical concept of *stationarity*.

Therefore, in areas that have stable or slowly changing patterns, AI is most effective. For example, consider natural language processing (NLP). There, AI has been very successful in processing and analyzing natural language data. The OpenAI GPT series is an example of a generative AI model focused on NLP. One factor in such successes is that language patterns change slowly. Further, we have a huge amount of possible training data in the form of books, blogs, newspapers, websites, and so on. Similarly, when it comes to biology and medicine, we are dealing with relatively stable systems. Therefore, AI could, for example, be effective in disease diagnosis.

On the other hand, when it comes to societal issues, we do not have stationarity. Earlier, we discussed that a major strength of current ML is its flexibility. ML parameters are tunable, so an ML model is not just one computer program but rather a large collection of programs. But let's not forget, an AI is still a model—a flexible model, yes, but still a model. Social events such as business environments, political climates, and social behaviors are complex, chaotic, and evolving; they are not easily described by models. This is why extra care is needed when applying ML in such fields.

3. THE TAIL PROBLEM

I am 8 years old, in a shuttle bus heading to a gymnastics summer camp with about 10 other kids ranging from 6 to 10 years old. None of us are wearing seatbelts. The shuttle is passing through a busy part of the city where everyone drives very aggressively and fast. The car is moving along a curved path when, out of nowhere, the sliding door opens by itself.

Suddenly, 10 kids are exposed to incredible danger. Due to the curve of the car's motion, some of the kids' stuff is thrown out into the middle of the busy road, and I, sitting next to the open door, am about to follow. Only by gripping the seat for dear life do I manage to stay put and avoid being flung from the vehicle.

Just as suddenly, all the vehicles close to us slow down or stop. I guess when you see a bunch of kids' stuff falling out of a shuttle bus with no door, you immediately understand you'd better slow down, no matter how aggressive a driver you are. I don't know about you, but as a driver, I have never faced a scenario like this, even though I have been driving for something like 1,000 years. Nevertheless, I'm pretty sure I would behave similarly to the drivers on that day.

Admittedly, this scenario is extremely rare and unlikely—but if we are to trust technologies like self-driving cars, it is crucial that any AI-powered driver be able to get these rare scenarios right. We humans do not need to have faced similar scenarios before to know how to handle them when they arise. This is because we have a basic understanding of how society works. However, at its current level, AI mostly learns by imitation; it does not truly understand what's going on around it. This means that it may have difficulty handling rare or unlikely scenarios like the one above, since it may not have encountered similar or comparable cases in the training data. These unusual, unique, and rare scenarios are sometimes referred to as *edge cases*.

Note that this rarity is a separate problem from the issue of stationarity. With an edge case, the environment could be completely stationary. That is, the statistical behaviors might not change at all. Nevertheless, due to their rareness, the AI may not have observed those edge cases before, so it may not know how to react appropriately.

AI DECISION-MAKING: AI TAKING ACTIONS

As you have probably deduced, self-driving cars differ in a significant way from some of the other AI examples we discussed. AI in cars does not just predict something; it *takes action* based on its prediction. This is a significant distinction, and it takes us to the important issue of AI decision-making.

Taking specific actions is the last step in the decision-making process and arguably the most crucial one. Choosing a specific action needs judgment and evaluation of possible outcomes and the risks and rewards associated with that action. Care is needed in making sure that such AI decisions are aligned with human values and do not have unwanted consequences.[16] This prompts us to discuss some AI risks.

SOME OTHER AI RISKS

Let's quickly recap our discussions on risks related to AI. In previous chapters, we discussed some threats to privacy; this is one aspect of AI risks. In this chapter, we've briefly mentioned AI bias and the alignment problem

16 This is the so-called alignment problem discussed extensively in Brian Christian's insightful book *The Alignment Problem*.

and discussed the potential impact of AI on jobs. Now, with these issues in mind, let's look more deeply at the idea of AI risks.

Another important source of risk in integrating AI too heavily into our lives is the *transparency problem*. When we write traditional rule-based programs, we know exactly how they work. But with ML, the algorithm is not always easy for us to interpret. Remember that in the training phase, some parameters are adjusted to fit the training data. However, in a complex ML model, we usually don't have much insight into why a particular set of parameters works, so we don't really understand what the resulting AI is doing. You can imagine how this lack of transparency could come with a host of issues and risks.

In addition, this transparency issue, combined with the limitations we discussed earlier, points to a particular kind of tail risk: we have a system that we might not fully understand and that might have limited common sense. This is why we have to be extra careful when putting AI systems in charge of any high-impact decisions.

LESSONS FOR BUSINESSES AND AI STRATEGY

Where does this AI risk discussion leave us in terms of good business AI strategies? One key point would be how we might integrate flexibility. Not investing enough in AI could be detrimental to a business whose competitors take full advantage of AI. On the other hand, overreliance on AI could expose the company to some of the risks we discussed.

If I were a business manager, I would try to adopt a strategy that gives me the highest flexibility as the field of AI evolves. I would first take small risks by playing around with AI and using randomization in small AI projects to see how they can help; those projects could then potentially turn into bigger ones. While doing so, I would keep in mind the pitfalls and risks we discussed in this chapter. All of these strategies tie into many of the concepts we discussed previously regarding risk management, the minimum assumption approach (MAA), and the benefits of randomization.

A FINAL LESSON FOR HUMANS FROM AI

Dear friend, now that we are almost at the end of our journey together, let me share with you an important lesson about human affairs that I have learned from considering AI. Remember that we discussed how AI usually learns from experience, and any time there is selection bias or any other kind of bias in the data (as with the penguin example), the AI may learn the wrong thing. Funnily enough, although we humans might be smarter than AI, we, too, are susceptible to learning the wrong lessons based on our own training data.

What is our training data? Well, our training data consists of all of our experiences. A tiny portion of that data comes from our formal education, but a bigger portion comes from our general life experience. Let's think about this for a minute. Of all the possible experiences in the world, you and I will experience an infinitesimal and insignificant portion of them during our lifetimes. Given this, how accurate can our learning possibly be? Can we really observe a true representative sample of reality?

This idea is mind boggling to me. With such a small and likely biased training data set, how can I know whether I have learned anything truly profound? How do I know that I am not detecting penguins by white backgrounds? This circles back to the uncertainty mindset we have discussed throughout this book. After everything we've considered, perhaps the conclusion we should reach here is that we should take the minimum assumption approach to decision-making. Another conclusion may be that we ought to be humble.

Here is another thing. It's not just that we each experience a tiny fraction of the world; it's that we all experience *different* tiny fractions. We each have our own tiny individual training data sets. Naturally, this means we learn different things. It's as simple as that. You and I are different; we have different beliefs and values, have different political opinions, support different football teams, and differ in just about every other way you can think of, mostly because we have different training data.

Here is my personal conclusion from this revelation: People are mostly different, but we are not better or worse than each other. A small fraction of life is objective, but a much bigger portion is subjective. Our differences simply depend on what training data each of us happens to observe.

I discussed in the previous chapter that I personally use uncertainty about free will to feel more compassionate toward others. But that is only part of the story. If

I am not careful, that philosophy could lead to self-righteousness. I might still assume that I can *judge* others, just not *dislike* them. From this discussion on our tiny and diverse personal training data, I think I can go much further. I'm not sure if you will reach the same conclusion as me, but I invite you, dear friend, to think about the ramifications of this issue as you go about implementing new strategies for making decisions in your life.

CHAPTER TAKEAWAYS

- A general understanding of AI and ML could be helpful to almost everyone. Machine learning is a subfield of artificial intelligence. The goal of ML is to give computers the ability to learn without explicitly being programmed.
- ML methods include supervised learning, unsupervised learning, and reinforcement learning (RL). In supervised learning, the computer learns by example. In unsupervised learning, the computer learns by finding patterns or structures in the input data. In RL, the computer usually learns by trying different strategies and experiences.
- One key concept of the supervised learning paradigm is that of tunable or flexible mappings: mappings with adjustable parameters. This flexibility is a primary reason for ML power.
- A tunable mapping can be thought of as a bag of mappings, each with a different set of values for the adjustable parameters.
- During the ML process, the adjustable parameters are automatically tuned according to the

training data. Equivalently, we can think of this tuning process as choosing an appropriate mapping from the bag of mappings.

- Big data, increases in computing power, improvements in learning algorithms, and new combinations of AI have all increased the effectiveness of ML in the past few decades.
- A complex or flexible model can be thought of as a bag with many mappings. The large number of mappings means that the bag is more likely to contain a suitable mapping for the desired task. However, it is also more likely that the bag contains other mappings that return good results on the training data merely by chance (overfitting).
- More complex models are more prone to overfitting, which means that due to the high complexity and flexibility of our model, we are actually fitting the noise, randomness, or idiosyncrasy of the training data.
- Cross validation, regularization, and training with more data are among measures we can use to reduce overfitting.
- In environments where there is high uncertainty or variability, simpler models are usually more robust and safer. The 1/N rule and its variations discussed in this book are examples of these safer approaches. Satisficing can also be justified from this perspective.
- The ability to handle subtleties such as overfitting, sampling bias, curse of dimensionality,

and data-snooping is a true and valuable skill for anyone working in ML.

- Since ML learns from data, any bias in the data can transfer to ML.
- Sampling bias is a widespread phenomenon that affects both AI and human decision-making.
- One way to spot sampling bias is to ask what unseen data may be missing from our analysis.
- In ML language, making a prediction means reducing uncertainty. This prediction could be about the past, present, or future.
- While very powerful, current AI capabilities have some limitations, including limited understanding, the slow change assumption, and the tail problem. Being aware of these limitations can guide us in determining what problems are best suited for AI.
- Some risks involved in employing AI include the potential for AI bias, privacy issues, issues of limited transparency, limited common (human) sense, ethics, and the alignment problem in general. Combined, these issues point to the possibility of a tail risk and show why we have to be extra careful when putting AI in charge of any high-impact decisions.
- Personally, I generally advocate for flexible strategies when employing AI: implementing trial and error, applying randomization, using the minimum assumption approach, and avoiding irreversible and potentially ruinous risks.
- We can think of all of our life experiences as our

training data. We experience a very tiny fraction of the world; even if we assume we have a perfect learning algorithm (our brain), this points to a huge limitation on what we learn.

- Each of us experiences our own specific training data set. This is one reason that each of us is different. Humility, the uncertainty mindset, and more tolerance of different opinions might be among the approaches we employ in our lives as we draw conclusions from this observation.

CONCLUSION

A few nights ago, my wife was out running some errands, and I was home with our two daughters. I prepared dinner, and we all sat down to eat. After about 15 minutes, something peculiar happened. I heard the most unexpected request from my kids. Did I hear my kids correctly? I asked them to repeat what they said, and they repeated loudly, "More kales!"

How is this possible? Kids are supposed to say, "more fries," "more ice cream," or "more candies"—not "more kales!" I was filled with a sense of pride. I told myself, "My wife and I are good parents! We have been careful about our kids' diet, so our kids learned to love kale!" I was telling myself all this BS when I suddenly realized the embarrassing truth: their "more kale" request was indicative of my generally bad cooking, not how much my kids loved kale! When kale is the most desirable part of a dish, the logical conclusion is not pretty.

The above incident is, of course, an example of Bayesian reasoning, one of the many topics we discussed in this book: conditioned on the observed data (kale request), we should choose the hypothesis with the highest probability (bad cooking), not the hypothesis we might like to accept (good parenting).

Looking at this story more broadly, we are reminded that unexpected events such as the request for more kale, do happen due to our inherent uncertainty, the subject of this book. Now, we are very close to the end of our journey to better understand uncertainty. We examined many topics together with a lot of details and nuances and, along the way, discussed many actionable ideas. I hope you have found some of those ideas useful (and the end-of-chapter takeaways can be helpful in reviewing some of the key ideas we covered). I am not going to summarize the whole content here; instead, I would just like to reemphasize one of the key messages in this book.

Yes, life is full of uncertainties, and there is much that we can neither predict nor control. Nevertheless, a key message in this book is that we *can* significantly improve our odds of favorable outcomes, specifically in the long run. We can do this, for example:

- by better understanding and appreciating uncertainty and randomness;
- by learning to be confident and uncertain at the same time;
- by incorporating insurance, margins, and flexibility in our lives;
- by understanding the power of LLN and improving our daily habits;
- by not being afraid of small failures and being willing to try new things;

- by persevering and making repeated attempts when it comes to important goals;
- by being continuously on the lookout for opportunities related to our major goals;
- by being aware of scenarios where many small individual risks create a big risk;
- by better understanding nonlinearity in life and work;
- by taking advantage of exponential growth opportunities;
- by avoiding harmful exponential growth situations via early detection and prevention;
- by understanding AI, as well as its strengths, weaknesses, and risks; and
- by many other general or specific ideas we have discussed in our journey together.

Dear friend, I am honored that you are still reading! If you have found some of the ideas presented in this book interesting or useful, I invite you to help spread them by sharing those ideas directly, recommending or reviewing this book, or any other way you deem appropriate. Thank you for taking the time to read this book.

Additional resources and information can be found at practicaluncertainty.com and probabilitycourse.com.

APPENDIX A:

SHANNON ENTROPY

In chapter 3, we mentioned that Shannon entropy is a measure of the uncertainty and randomness associated with a set of possible outcomes. Let us discuss this concept a little more. The intuitive idea behind Shannon entropy is given by the idea of *the average surprise*. Here, the *average* is computed assuming the experiment is repeated a large number of times.

In the context of binary events—say, getting into an accident when driving to work—most of the time, there is very little surprise. Most days, when we drive to work, we do not get into an accident. Once in a while, we might get a huge surprise, i.e., an accident. But the average surprise is still very low because most days are accident-free. Thus, for low-probability events such as accidents when driving to work, the entropy is low.

Similarly, for high-probability events—say, your car starting in the morning—the average surprise is still low. Most days, your car starts with no problem, so there is very little surprise on most days. Occasionally, you might get a big surprise when your car won't start in the morning. Again due to the rarity of those bad days, the average surprise is still low.

It turns out the maximum average surprise occurs when the event probability gets closer to 50%. For such events, we are moderately surprised every day, so the average surprise is higher than it is for low-probability and high-probability events.

To further internalize this concept, you can imagine randomly selecting marbles from a big bag of marbles. You are interested in the color of marbles you select from the bag. Two factors could determine the amount of uncertainty or the average surprise: (1) the number of distinct colors and (2) the portion of colors.

If all marbles are black, the average surprise is zero. Now, if you add some white marbles to the bag, entropy increases (higher average surprise = higher uncertainty)

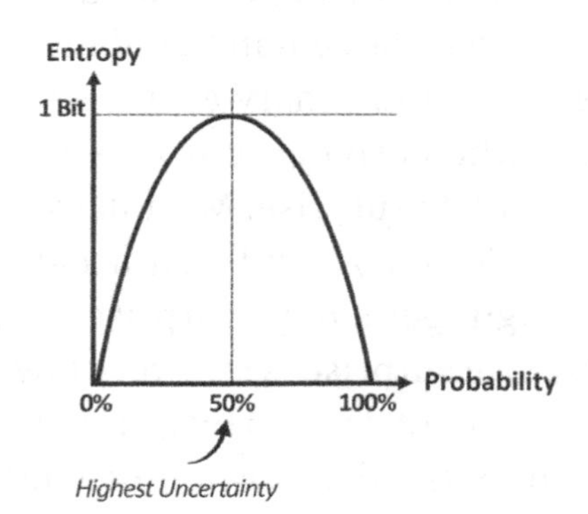

Figure A.1: Binary entropy function. The maximum average surprise occurs when an event probability is 50%.

In the case of black and white marbles, the maximum entropy is obtained when half of the marbles are black and the other half are white.

You can further increase the entropy by adding more colors, maybe by adding some blue marbles to the bag. Given that there are now three distinct colors, the entropy is maximized when each color represents one third of the marbles.

One interesting observation is that entropy depends only on the probability of possible outcomes and not on their magnitudes. This is why it is not a sufficient factor for decision-making. This is why we have spent a lot of time in this book discussing high-impact events, even though such events could technically be rare and have very low entropy.

For the interested reader, the formula for Shannon entropy of a binary variable X is given by

$$H(X) = -p \log_2 p - (1 - p) \log_2(1 - p),$$

where p is the probability of $X = 1$. More generally, for a discrete random variable X, Shannon entropy is defined as

$$H(X) = -E[\log_2 P(X)],$$

where $P(X)$ is the probability mass function of X.

APPENDIX B: SOME GENERAL ML APPROACHES

ML is a huge area with many subfields. In chapter 7, I focused on key ideas that I found most essential and useful. Here, I provide some background regarding a few important concepts that I did not cover in that chapter.

THE BAYESIAN APPROACH TO ML

ML comes in different flavors. Our discussion on uncertainty provides the basis for an important approach in ML that you're already familiar with: the Bayesian approach. Remember, from chapter 6, the idea behind Bayes' rule: You start with some *initial belief*, usually called your *prior probability*. Then, using Bayes' rule, you update your probability based on the *evidence* at hand. In other words, with Bayes' rule, you can reduce your uncertainty.

This idea can be applied in a variety of ways. Say you would like to design a spam filter that automatically categorizes emails as spam or non-spam. Here, the initial belief could simply be the probability of spam given no observation. If, for example, around 50% of emails are spam, you could use this value as the prior probability.

Then, the evidence could be the words or phrases in the email that your program tries to classify. Knowing that some words or phrases are more common in spam emails, you might proceed as follows.

For your training data, you collect a large group of emails that are carefully labeled as "spam" or "non-spam." For each word or phrase, you compute the percentages of their appearance in spam and non-spam emails. These percentages essentially give you the probabilities of each phrase given that the email is spam or non-spam. Your program can then use Bayes' rule to compute the probability that an email with certain phrases is either spam or non-spam.

Another way to apply the Bayesian approach is in the mapping selection itself. Let's consider our bag of mappings. We can start by assigning some prior probability to each of the mappings in the bag. In this case, the evidence could be our training data. Using Bayes' rule and the training data, we can then update our probabilities. Specifically, mappings that are more consistent with the training data would get higher probabilities.

A key aspect of the Bayesian approach is that we need a prior. If you can somehow justify your choice of prior, then the Bayesian method could be promising. The Bayesian approach has been used in many applications including spam filtering, medical diagnosis, error-correcting codes, and image processing.

PROBABILISTIC ML

Bayesian ML can be considered a subclass of *probabilistic machine learning*. Probabilistic ML is a field that includes any machine learning method that is based on probabilistic models. Probabilistic ML methods primarily aim to estimate the probability distribution that generated the data. Large language models, such as the GPT series, are often considered examples of probabilistic models. A central concept in these models involves predicting the next word given a preceding sequence of words. This prediction is derived by assigning probabilities based on vast amounts of text used for training the model.

UNSUPERVISED LEARNING

One way to categorize general approaches to ML is as follows:

1. Supervised learning
2. Unsupervised learning
3. Reinforcement learning

We discussed the first approach, *supervised learning*, in detail in chapter 7. Using labeled data, we train a standard tunable mapping to perform the task we want it to do.

The second approach to ML is called *unsupervised learning*. In these scenarios, we do not have labeled data or examples (X, Y); we just have the input data X. Usually, the main goal is to find patterns or structures in the input data. This is sometimes called *knowledge discovery*.

A prominent example of unsupervised learning is clustering. Here, we organize the input data into groups to discover features or structures. For example, let's say you run a very large company that has had millions of customers over the years, and you want to learn more about these customers. One way of learning more is to group them into different categories. Maybe certain segments of customers behave similarly, and you can cluster customers based on their behavior into three groups. Based on this grouping technique, you can understand their behaviors better, perhaps to provide different promotions to these customers.

Essentially, this is called clustering because we are only given some input data. We don't have any labels Y; we just group these customers into different categories.

Another example of clustering that you might be familiar with is news aggregator services such as Google News. These services usually give you multiple links for the relevant stories of the day, each from a different news organization. Clustering algorithms are usually used to discover news articles that talk about the same type of events. Thus, in general, information is clustered into different segments or categories, each of which contains similar objects.

In the development of large language models, a step known as pre-training is typically incorporated. During pre-training, the model is exposed to vast amounts of internet text, enabling it to learn grammar, semantics, and general knowledge. This pre-training phase is often classified as *self-supervised* learning. Self-supervised learning uses unlabeled data like unsupervised learning but generates its own labels, resembling supervised learning.

REINFORCEMENT LEARNING

Another approach is *reinforcement learning* (RL), which refers to the process of learning through experiences. Consider how a child may learn not to touch a hot cup of coffee. The child would face a negative reward for touching the hot cup, the consequence being a high level of inflicted pain. When the child does not touch the hot cup, there is no pain. Eventually, after a few tries, the child will learn that it is better to leave the hot cup of coffee alone.

In terms of RL, the child is an agent that interacts with an environment (the hot cup of coffee) and learns by taking actions (touch or not touch) that maximizes the reward (no pain). The training examples did not have labels declaring what the toddler should do but instead graded the different actions that were made. This is how we characterize RL: the examples contain not the target output but instead some measurement of how good the output is. The RL algorithm sorts out different information coming from different examples or experiences to find the best policy based on the rewards obtained.

Another example we can use to describe RL is the process of learning to ride a bike on your own: you might try different tactics each time you get on the bike and ultimately stick with the approach that keeps you upright for the longest time.

RL has also been used successfully in gaming. For example, DeepMind—a leader in AI research that is owned by Google—designed the first computer program to ever beat a professional player in the game of Go (known as one of the most challenging classical games for artificial intelligence because of its complexity). They used RL to train the program to take actions that maximize the expected reward.

RECOMMENDED READING

Abu-Mostafa, Yaser S., Malik-Magdon-Ismail, and Hsuan-Tien Lin. *Learning From Data.* AMLBook, 2012.

Aczel, Amir D. Chance. *A Guide to Gambling, Love, the Stock Market, and Just About Everything Else*. New York: Basic Books, 2004.

Ariely, Dan. *Predictably Irrational: The Hidden Forces That Shape Our Decisions*. London: HarperCollins UK, 2005.

Baer, Tobias. *Understand, Manage, and Prevent Algorithmic Bias: A Guide for Business Users and Data Scientists*. New York: Apress, 2019.

Banaji, Mahzarin R., and Anthony G. Greenwald. *Blindspot: Hidden Biases of Good People*. London: Bantam, 2016.

Barabási, Albert-László. *The Formula: The Universal Laws of Success*. Boston: Little, Brown and Company, 2018.

Bennett, Deborah J. *Randomness*. Cambridge, MA: Harvard University Press, 1998.

Buss, David. *Evolutionary Psychology: The New Science of the Mind*. London: Psychology Press, 2015.

Chabris, Christopher, and Daniel Simons. *The Invisible Gorilla: And Other Ways Our Intuition Deceives Us*. London: HarperCollins UK, 2010.

Christakis, Nicholas A., and James H. Fowler. *Connected: The Surprising Power of Our Social Networks and How They Shape Our Lives—How Your Friends' Friends' Friends Affect Everything You Feel, Think, and Do*. Reprint ed. Boston: Little Brown Spark, 2011.

Christian, Brian. *The Alignment Problem: Machine Learning and Human Values*. W. W. Norton & Company, 2020.

Christian, Brian, and T. Griffiths. *Algorithms to Live By: The Computer Science of Human Decisions*. London: HarperCollins UK, 2016.

Clear, James. *Atomic Habits: An Easy & Proven Way to Build Good Habits & Break Bad Ones*. New York: Avery, 2018.

Cover, Thomas, and Joy Thomas. *Elements of Information Theory*. 2nd ed. Hoboken, NJ: Wiley-Interscience, 2006.

Domingos, Pedro. *The Master Algorithm: How the Quest for the Ultimate Learning Machine Will Remake Our World*. London: Basic Books, 2015.

Duckworth, Angela. *Grit: The Power of Passion and Perseverance*. New York: Scribner, 2016.

Duhigg, Charles. *The Power of Habit: Why We Do What We Do in Life and Business*. New York: Random House, 2012.

Duke, Annie. *How to Decide: Simple Tools for Making Better Choices*. Portfolio Penguin, 2020.

———. "Make Better Decisions." Online course, Maven, 2022. https://maven.com/annie-duke/make-better-decisions.

———. *Quit: The Power of Knowing When to Walk Away*. Audible. New York: Penguin Audio, 2022.

———. *Thinking in Bets: Making Smarter Decisions When You Don't Have All the Facts*. New York: Penguin, 2019.

Dweck, Carol S. Mindset: *The New Psychology of Success*. New York: Ballantine Books, 2007.

Ellenberg, Jordan. *How Not to Be Wrong: The Power of Mathematical Thinking*. New York: National Geographic Books, 2015.

Fogg, BJ. *Tiny Habits: The Small Changes That Change Everything*. New York: HarperCollins, 2019.

Fry, Hannah. *Hello World: Being Human in the Age of Algorithms*. New York: W. W. Norton, 2018.

Galef, Julia. *The Scout Mindset: Why Some People See Things Clearly and Others Don't*. New York: Portfolio, 2021.

Gigerenzer, Gerd. *Risk Savvy: How to Make Good Decisions*. London: Penguin UK, 2014.

Gilboa, Itzhak. *Making Better Decisions: Decision Theory in Practice*. Hoboken, NJ: John Wiley & Sons, 2010.

Gladwell, Malcolm. *Outliers: The Story of Success*. Boston: Little, Brown and Company, 2008.

Grant, Adam. *Think Again: The Power of Knowing What You Don't Know*. New York: Random House, 2021.

Gunther, Max. *The Luck Factor: Why Some People Are Luckier Than Others and How You Can Become One of Them*. London: MacMillan Publishing Company, 1977.

Harari, Yuval Noah. *21 Lessons for the 21st Century*. New York: Random House, 2018.

Hardy, Darren. *The Compound Effect*. New York: Vanguard Press, 2012.

Harris, Sam. *The Moral Landscape: How Science Can Determine Human Values*. New York: Simon and Schuster, 2010.

Heath, Chip, and Dan Heath. *Decisive: How to Make Better Choices in Life and Work*. London: Penguin UK, 2013.

Housel, Morgan. *The Psychology of Money: Timeless Lessons on Wealth, Greed, and Happiness*. Petersfield, UK: Harriman House Limited, 2020.

James, Gareth, Daniela Witten, Trevor Hastie, and Robert Tibshirani. *An Introduction to Statistical Learning: With Applications in R*. Berlin, Germany: Springer Science & Business Media, 2013.

Jaynes, E. T. Probability Theory: The Logic of Science. Edited by G. Larry Bretthorst. Cambridge, MA: Cambridge University Press, 2003.

Kahneman, Daniel. *Thinking, Fast and Slow*. London: Penguin UK, 2011.

Kay, John, and Mervyn King. *Radical Uncertainty: Decision-Making Beyond the Numbers*. New York: W. W. Norton & Company, 2020.

Konnikova, Maria. *The Confidence Game: Why We Fall for It . . . Every Time*. Reprint ed. New York: Penguin Books, 2017.

Lockwood, David. *Fooled by the Winners: How Survivor Bias Deceives Us*. Austin, TX: Greenleaf Book Group, 2021.

Mandelbrot, Benoit, and Richard L. Hudson. *The Misbehavior of Markets: A Fractal View of Financial Turbulence*. Annotated ed. New York: Basic Books, 2006.

Matthews, Robert. *Chancing It: The Laws of Chance and How They Can Work For You*. London: Profile Books, 2017.

McChrystal, General Stanley, and Anna Butrico. *Risk: A User's Guide*. London: Penguin UK, 2021.

Milkman, Katy. *How to Change: The Science of Getting from Where You Are to Where You Want to Be*. New York: Random House, 2021.

Mitchell, Melanie. *Artificial Intelligence: A Guide for Thinking Humans*. London: Penguin UK, 2019.

Mlodinow, Leonard. *Emotional: How Feelings Shape Our Thinking*.

New York: National Geographic Books, 2023.
———. *The Drunkard's Walk: How Randomness Rules Our Lives*. London: Vintage, 2009.

Noble, Safiya Umoja. *Algorithms of Oppression: How Search Engines Reinforce Racism*. New York: NYU Press, 2018.

Olofsson, Peter. *Probabilities: The Little Numbers That Rule Our Lives*. Hoboken, NJ: John Wiley & Sons, 2015.

O'Neil, Cathy. *Weapons of Math Destruction: How Big Data Increases Inequality and Threatens Democracy*. New York: Crown Publishing Group, 2017.

Osoba, Osonde A., and William Welser IV. *An Intelligence in Our Image: The Risks of Bias and Errors in Artificial Intelligence*. Santa Monica, CA: Rand Corporation, 2017.

Peterson, Martin. *An Introduction to Decision Theory*. Cambridge, MA: Cambridge University Press, 2017.

Pinker, Steven. Rationality: *What It Is, Why It Seems Scarce, Why It Matters*. London: Penguin UK, 2021.

Pishro-Nik, Hossein. *Introduction to Probability, Statistics, and Random Processes*. Sunderland, MA: Kappa Research, LLC, 2014. https://www.probabilitycourse.com/.

Rosenthal, Jeffrey S. *Struck By Lightning: The Curious World of Probabilities*. London: Granta Books, 2006.

Rosenzweig, Phil. *The Halo Effect: . . . And the Eight Other Business Delusions That Deceive Managers*. New York: Simon and Schuster, 2014.

Shane, Janelle. *You Look Like a Thing and I Love You: How Artificial Intelligence Works and Why It's Making the World a Weirder Place*. London: Hachette UK, 2019.

Silver, Nate. *The Signal and the Noise: The Art and Science of Prediction*. London: Penguin UK, 2012.

Smith, Gary. *Standard Deviations: Flawed Assumptions, Tortured Data and Other Ways to Lie with Statistics*. London: Bloomsbury Academic, 2016.

Spitznagel, Mark. *Safe Haven: Investing for Financial Storms*. Hoboken, NJ: John Wiley & Sons, 2021.

Taleb, Nassim Nicholas. *Antifragile: Things That Gain from Disorder*. London: Penguin UK, 2012.

———. *The Black Swan: The Impact of the Highly Improbable*. 2nd ed. New York: Random House Publishing Group, 2010.

———. *Fooled by Randomness: The Hidden Role of Chance in Life and in the Markets*. London: Penguin UK, 2007.

———. *Skin in the Game: Hidden Asymmetries in Daily Life*. London: Penguin UK, 2018.

Taleb, Nassim Nicholas, Robert J. Frey, and Raphael Douady. "Real World Risk Institute," 2015. https://realworldrisk.com/.

Tetlock, Philip E., and Dan Gardner. *Superforecasting: The Art and Science of Prediction*. New York: Random House, 2016.

Thaler, Richard H. *Misbehaving: The Making of Behavioural Economics*. London: W. W. Norton & Company, 2015.

Theobald, Oliver. *Machine Learning for Absolute Beginners: A Plain English Introduction*. Independently Published, 2018.

Tracy, Brian. *Eat That Frog!: 21 Great Ways to Stop Procrastinating and Get More Done in Less Time*. Oakland, CA: Berrett-Koehler Publishers, 2017.

Wolfram, Stephen. *What Is ChatGPT Doing . . . and Why Does It Work?* Champaign, IL: Wolfram Media, Inc., 2023.

ACKNOWLEDGMENTS

Ashleigh Daher, Liz Chadwick, Sarah Kolb-Williams, Britt Peterson, Shane Schwartz, Elias Sink, Marco Duarte, Ali Khayati, Sepideh Sakhaeifar, Pratusha Nouduri, Emily Ruf, my students, my family, and all the scholars I learned from.

ABOUT THE AUTHOR

Hossein Pishro-Nik is a professor in the Department of Electrical and Computer Engineering at the University of Massachusetts Amherst. His research interests include information theory, networks of autonomous agents, statistical learning, and decision-making. He is the author of a popular textbook titled *Introduction to Probability, Statistics, and Random Processes*, which is freely available at www.probabilitycourse.com.

Pishro-Nik has won some awards, but more importantly, he has had spectacular failures: He was once expelled from high school for trying to be funny in a serious meeting. He was once put in charge of the barbecue at a party, but after burning half of the burgers, he was discharged of the responsibility by unanimous vote. He thinks he is a good soccer player, but he is not.

Made in the USA
Middletown, DE
11 December 2023